LIFE SCIENCE LIBRARY

THE ENGINEER

TIME
LIFE
BOOKS
®

LIFE SCIENCE LIBRARY

CONSULTING EDITORS
René Dubos
Henry Margenau
C. P. Snow

THE ENGINEER

by C. C. Furnas, Joe McCarthy
and the Editors of TIME-LIFE BOOKS

TIME-LIFE BOOKS   NEW YORK

ABOUT THIS BOOK

THE WORLD'S ENGINEERS have probably contributed more to the shaping of civilization than any other group of men. For in every society, the engineer's role is to develop, from the knowledge of his day, technological applications which meet practical needs: a waterwheel to power a mill; an electrical system to light a city; an artificial heart to prolong life. This book shows how the engineer has changed over the centuries from an ingenious improviser who worked by trial and error, to a skilled and systematic specialist who brings a wealth of scientific knowledge to bear on the increasingly complex problems of today and tomorrow.

Each chapter has a supplementary picture essay which may be read independently. For example, Chapter 2, "The 'Old Man' and His Helpers," explores the traditional, intuitive approach to engineering. It is followed by a picture essay, "The Wizard of Menlo Park," which discusses Thomas Edison as an engineer who bridged the gap between the skilled tinkerer and the modern science-oriented professional.

THE AUTHORS

C. C. FURNAS was for many years President of the State University of New York at Buffalo. A chemical engineer, he did research in aeronautical engineering and served as Assistant Secretary of Defense for Research and Development from 1955 to 1957. He also wrote several books, including *America's Tomorrow*.

JOE McCARTHY, a former correspondent and managing editor of the Army's weekly magazine *Yank* in World War II, has been a freelance writer since 1948. His books include *The Remarkable Kennedys* and the LIFE World Library's *Ireland*.

THE CONSULTING EDITORS

RENÉ DUBOS, a member and professor of The Rockefeller University, is a distinguished microbiologist and experimental pathologist who was awarded the Arches of Science Award in 1966. His books include *Mirage of Health* and *Man Adapting*. He is also coauthor of *Health and Disease* in this series.

HENRY MARGENAU is Eugene Higgins Professor of Physics and Natural Philoso-

phy at Yale, and an authority in spectroscopy and nuclear physics. He wrote *Open Vistas, The Nature of Physical Reality,* and is coauthor of *The Scientist* in this series.

C. P. SNOW has won an international audience for his novels, including *The New Men, The Affair* and *Corridors of Power,* which explore the effects of science on today's society.

ON THE COVER

Building the Verrazano-Narrows Bridge, which has the world's longest central suspension span, was facilitated by the precise tools and sophisticated techniques of modern engineering. Yet its engineers relied also on their ingenuity, as did their ancient predecessors, who made do with simple tools like the plumb-bob level on the back cover.

CONTENTS

INTRODUCTION 7

1 **A MAN OF MANY TALENTS**   8
Picture Essay: 12,000 Engineers to Make a Car 16

2 **THE "OLD MAN" AND HIS HELPERS**   32
Picture Essay: The Wizard of Menlo Park 40

3 **FROM PYRAMID TO TELEGRAPH**   54
Picture Essay: Durable Works of Ancient Engineers 62

4 **THE MODERN METHOD: SYSTEMS ENGINEERING**   76
Picture Essay: Education without End 86

5 **SKYSCRAPERS, RADOMES AND CHIPS**   100
Picture Essay: The Challenge of a Great Bridge 108

6 **WASTE NOT, WANT NOT**   122
Picture Essay: The Most for the Least 132

7 **THE HUMAN FACTOR**   144
Picture Essay: Building Machines to Fit Men 154

8 **THE TOUGH PROBLEMS AHEAD**   170
Picture Essay: Designs for the Year 2000 178

Great Engineers of Recent Centuries 193
Further Reading and Acknowledgments 196
Index 197
Picture Credits 200

TIME-LIFE BOOKS

EDITOR
Jerry Korn
EXECUTIVE EDITOR
A. B. C. Whipple
PLANNING
Oliver E. Allen

TEXT DIRECTOR   ART DIRECTOR
Martin Mann   Sheldon Cotler
CHIEF OF RESEARCH
Beatrice T. Dobie
DIRECTOR OF PHOTOGRAPHY
Robert G. Mason
Assistant Text Directors:
Ogden Tanner, Diana Hirsh
Assistant Art Director: Arnold C. Holeywell
Assistant Chief of Research: Martha T. Goolrick
Assistant Director of Photography: Melvin L. Scott

PUBLISHER
Joan D. Manley
General Manager: John D. McSweeney
Business Manager: John Steven Maxwell
Sales Director: Carl G. Jaeger
Promotion Director: Beatrice K. Tolleris
Public Relations Director: Nicholas Benton

LIFE SCIENCE LIBRARY

SERIES EDITOR: Martin Mann
Editorial staff for *The Engineer:*
Associate Editor: Robert G. Mason
Text Editors: L. Robert Tschirky, Leon Greene,
Nancy E. Gross, Charles Osborne
Picture Editor: Anthony Wolff
Designer: Edwin Taylor
Associate Designer: Charles Mikolaycak
Staff Writers: Timothy Carr, Peter M. Chaitin,
George Constable, Jonathan Kastner,
Marianna Pinchot, Bryce S. Walker
Chief Researcher: Helen Fennell
Researchers: Roxanna Sayre, Mollie Cooper,
Sally Draper, Elizabeth A. Freilich,
Joan Gerard, Rosemary Haverland,
Melvin Ingber, Pamela Johnson, Alice Kantor,
Carole Kismaric, Robert Liang, James MaHood,
Melissa Wanamaker

EDITORIAL PRODUCTION
Production Editor: Douglas B. Graham
Quality Director: Robert L. Young
Assistant: James J. Cox
Copy Staff: Rosalind Stubenberg,
Suzanne Seixas, Florence Keith
Picture Department: Dolores A. Littles,
Barbara Sullivan
Art Assistants: Kumiko Maeda,
Raymond Ripper

This book, from its conception to final editing, was under the professional direction of C. C. Furnas. The text chapters were written by Joe McCarthy, the picture essays by the editorial staff. The following individuals and departments of Time Inc. were helpful in the production of the book: LIFE staff photographers Robert W. Kelley, Dmitri Kessel, Leonard McCombe, Francis Miller and Ralph Morse; Editorial Production, Robert W. Boyd Jr., Margaret T. Fischer; Editorial Reference, Peter Draz; Picture Collection, Doris O'Neil; Photographic Laboratory, George Karas; TIME-LIFE News Service, Murray J. Gart. Reprints Staff: Paula Arno (editor), Alice Kantor and Carolyn Tasker (assistant editors).

INTRODUCTION

IN THIS AGE OF WONDERS, the citizen bombarded with tales of the still-more miraculous isn't quite sure whether he is looking through an Alice-in-Wonderland mirror or experiencing reality. He understands little except the result, but is happy to accept it. But does he appreciate that the result is the work of the engineer, that the engineer is a doer, a builder, a creator, and that the engineer serves man by converting the materials and forces of nature to his purpose?

As in all professions, a few lead and many follow. So the stories of the great men and grand accomplishments of engineering become the story of the profession. In this book the leaders have been well chosen. Their stories are so told that any intelligent reader may come to comprehend the engineering method and how it is making it possible for all of us to do more living in a given life-span than we once could—that is, to have richer lives.

The engineering method combines experience with theory and provides self-testing of the critical components. It is the weaving together of all of these. Fortified by the computer, it analyzes and attacks situations of ever-increasing complexity, situations that involve whole systems. And systems engineering is the engineer's new working tool. Today systems engineering is applied to economics, politics and people as well as to things.

Engineering has solved many difficult problems of the past. If we are to solve our even more difficult ones posed by mass education, urban development, the war against poverty, if we are to build a great society, we must use the new working tool of the engineer. With it we can build a better world, build the bridge from things to people. The essence of the engineering approach is well illustrated in this simple, delightful, enlightening exposition of the ways leading engineers through the ages have applied both the older and the newer methods so successfully.

—AUGUSTUS B. KINZEL
Founding President, National Academy of Engineering

1
A Man
of Many Talents

A First Century A.D. Roman engineer's tools—an A-frame, a ruler, a plumb line, calipers and a set square—are carved on his tomb.

"THE ENGINEER typifies the twentieth century," said Alfred P. Sloan Jr., for many years President of the General Motors Corporation. "Without his genius and the vast contributions he has made in design, engineering, and production on the material side of our existence, our contemporary life could never have reached its present standard."

The proof of Sloan's proud statement is visible all around us. The systems that supply our food, water, fuel and power; our networks of transportation, communication and defense; many of the devices that help to cure our diseases and some that prolong lives; our push-button home entertainment—these and countless other necessities and conveniences are the products of engineering skill. Yet despite the essential part the engineer plays in the progress and well-being of humanity, to many he is a blurred figure, his exact role imperfectly understood.

One reason for the hazy impression left by the modern engineer is his close association with the scientist. Both men look alike, talk alike, worry over similar mathematical equations; the guard at the plant gate who checks their identification badges often cannot tell which is which. In fact, in such industries as plastics and communications, it is difficult to determine where the scientist's work ends and the engineer's begins.

The basic distinction between the linked professions of science and engineering lies in their goals. The scientist aims to discover new knowledge, whether useful or not, while the engineer strives to put knowledge, old or new, to work efficiently for the needs of mankind. Thus a scientist, the German physicist Heinrich Hertz, discovered radio waves, but Guglielmo Marconi developed wireless telegraphy, a feat of engineering. And after the scientific principles of nuclear fission were established, the hard work of creating atomic weapons and useful power plants was accomplished by electrical, chemical and mechanical engineers.

This description of the engineer may make him seem dependent on the scientist, earning his living by developing ideas produced in the scientist's laboratory. In reality, however, scientists are just as dependent upon the work of engineers as the other way round; many great discoveries of science have stemmed from engineering. For example, the fundamentals of thermodynamics, the science of heat, were established by Nicolas Léonard Sadi Carnot, a French physicist who studied the practical steam engines that had already been developed by engineers who had no science to guide them.

There is another reason why it is difficult to bring the engineer into sharp focus. He is a man of many talents. Some engineers—fewer now than in the past—are loners. Others are narrow specialists; one consulting engineer, for instance, bases his practice entirely on a single function, the installation of air-conditioning units in rooms for computers. But many of today's engineers are broad-gauge executives, managers skilled in several technologies and able to combine and coordinate teams of specialists. And a successful engineer must often be a successful salesman; unless he can convince nonengineers to put his ideas or devices to work, his efforts will have been wasted.

One basic quality, however, is found in every engineer. He is first of all a practical man, a pragmatist who shoulders the mundane problems of civilization—and solves them. He gets the job done, efficiently and economically, although he may reach his goal by any of a variety of paths. Paradoxically, this practical man may be a visionary who dreams of a better way to do the job; who uses his creative ingenuity to establish a totally new system or applies an old method in a new and imaginative way. Sometimes his solution is simple, a seemingly trivial bit of invention easily dismissed as tinkering—but the engineer's tinkering frequently reaches an inspired level.

Practicality, vision, salesmanship and inventiveness—these and other characteristics of the great engineers can best be illustrated by the stories of the men themselves. Some have displayed one trait more clearly than another, but all have helped make the world we live in today.

The single-mindedness of the lonely worker, for example, has led to great achievement and has inspired legend. When John Roebling, the builder of the Brooklyn Bridge, was busy completing his Niagara suspension bridge in 1854, he learned with surprise that his wife had given birth to a child several days previously. While Jacob Rabinow, a prolific inventor-engineer, was on his honeymoon, he took apart a faulty electric fan in his hotel room. By the time he had finished tinkering with the fan, Rabinow had worked out an idea for a reversing electric motor which can attain full speed in its new direction in less than two thousandths of a second.

In pursuit of a lofty goal

Yesterday's lonely inventors endured years of privation to work obsessively on the solution to a problem. Charles Goodyear's family often went without food and heat while he spent eight years searching for a method of curing rubber. At one point, when his wife and children had nothing to eat except potatoes and wild roots, he refused a generous offer from France for his acid-gas curing process because, as he explained to the prospective customer, he was then working on something better than acid gas. In 1900 Lee De Forest threw up a $10-a-week job and lived on a five-dollar weekly handout from a friend and a few dollars from part-time teaching while he worked on wireless telegraphy in a Chicago rented room. He wrote in his diary at the time: "Twice have I renounced good and fairly promising positions for my faith in an idea and in myself. Risks have they been, and serious, for I am aging in years and will soon be twenty-eight. Money I have none, influence none, acquaintance none. In industry, diligence, I am not lacking, nor have lacked for many years. . . . Courage I have, while optimism has ever been a cardinal characteristic of my youth. Why then should I not take the risk and boldly strike . . . for a lofty mark?"

Among the notable accomplishments of the lone operators who worked out their own ideas, aided only by ingenuity, imagination and dogged persistence, one of the most startling is that of Philo Taylor Farnsworth.

He was only 15 years old in 1922 when he stayed after school one day to show the chemistry teacher in his small Idaho town a thoughtful scheme for television broadcasting, at that time considered impractical by professional engineers.

The boy had gained his entire knowledge of television from a sketchy magazine article that described the experiments conducted 20 years earlier by the Russian engineer Boris Rosing. In his laboratory, Rosing had been able to transmit and receive only a small, blurred picture by wire. Farnsworth's idea represented a great advance: he proposed building a camera that would accurately transform an image into electrical impulses for effective transmission. A few years later, although he was then still too young to sign a contract legally, Farnsworth had won financial backing. During the 1930s his only serious rival in television engineering was Vladimir Zworykin, an engineer with the Radio Corporation of America. Zworykin, who had worked under Rosing in Russia, had developed a different approach. Farnsworth's syndicate and RCA reached an agreement in order to perfect and integrate the best features of both systems, and by 1946 television was entertaining and informing the nation.

Some 50 years before Farnsworth first read the article on television, another magazine article had similarly stimulated the imagination of George Westinghouse. Westinghouse, then a young engineer, was appalled by the perils of railroad travel, largely the result of undependable brakes. In those days, even if the locomotive engineer saw danger ahead, he had no way of stopping all the cars in his train simultaneously. Each car had its own hand brake and a brakeman who turned a wheel to slow the car when the engineer tooted a warning whistle. The varying speeds with which the brakemen responded made it practically impossible to bring the whole train to a sudden, safe halt; emergency stops usually meant derailment as cars piled up on each other.

Piped-air to halt trains

One day, as he sat in a stalled train and waited for the wreckage of two others to be cleared from the tracks ahead, Westinghouse began to think about how he could improve on the hand brakes. At first he experimented with a steam-operated, one-man control system that would brake all the cars at once, but that was unsuccessful. Then in 1867 the 21-year-old engineer happened to see a magazine article describing the use of pneumatic drills in tunneling through Mont Cenis in the Alps. These drills were fed compressed air pumped into the tunnel through thousands of feet of pipe. This method, Westinghouse realized, would solve his problems: air under pressure, piped along the entire length of the train, could be used to apply all brakes simultaneously at the touch of a lever in the locomotive cab.

After he had designed his air brakes, Westinghouse found that one of the engineer's most difficult problems is trying to sell a new idea. When the principle of air brakes was explained to Commodore Cornelius Vanderbilt of the New York Central, the railroad tycoon exclaimed, "Stop a

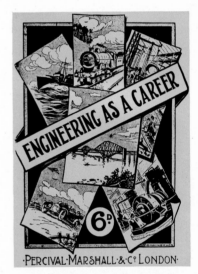

AN ENGINEERING MANUAL, published in England in 1916, illustrates some of the dozen different branches—such as marine, railway or construction engineering—then open to prospective students. Before a student could join an engineering firm, he trained for three or four years as an apprentice. Today a student spends four years in college and perhaps another four in graduate school before he is ready for a career in one of the hundreds of specialized areas of modern engineering.

locomotive with wind? I have no time to talk with fools!" But Westinghouse was as effective a salesman as an engineer, and his air-brake system was subsequently adopted by all American and foreign railroads.

For other engineers, such as the brilliant Oliver Evans of Philadelphia, the failure to convince others of the practical value of a new scheme meant heartbreak. Evans was an 18th Century visionary who was creative in an astonishing variety of fields, but whose ideas were usually too advanced for his time. In 1786, when he asked the Pennsylvania legislature for a patent on a horseless, steam-driven carriage, he was advised to stop such fantastic talk if he did not want to be judged insane. Evans had been experimenting with steam power since 1772, when he watched some boys setting off an explosion by filling a gun barrel with water, sealing the open end of the barrel with a stopper and then heating the breech in a fire. When the steam expanded within the barrel, the pressure blew the stopper out with a loud crack.

Philadelphia's amphibious wonder

Evans, undaunted by those who thought him a crackpot, predicted the day would come "when people will travel in stages moved by steam engines, from one city to another, almost as fast as birds fly, fifteen to twenty miles an hour." And in 1805 he succeeded in producing the first vehicle in America to move under its own power. It was a marvel for that time or any other—an amphibious vessel driven by steam. Actually it was a dredging scow; a steam engine propelled it forward on land and operated its digger and stern paddle wheel when the vehicle took to water. Evans christened it the *Orukter Amphibolos*, or the "amphibious digger." He exhibited the ungainly contraption—30 feet long and weighing 17 tons—by driving it from his Philadelphia workshop up Market Street and around Centre Square before steering it into the Schuylkill River and thence to the city's docks.

More significant than the strange appearance of the *Orukter Amphibolos* was the steam engine that drove it. Evans' engine was smaller than the atmospheric engines of James Watt and also more efficient because it took greater advantage of the steam it consumed. Instead of contenting himself with Watt's low steam pressures, which never rose much higher than the normal sea-level pressure of 14.7 pounds per inch, Evans used high-pressure steam in quick successive blasts to push the piston up and down. Some of the steam engines he built after 1805 for milling grain and turning riverboat paddles operated with steam pressures up to 150 pounds per inch. Although the engine proved sound, the dredge itself did not, and Evans' amphibious digger was abandoned.

Evans had a rare inventive genius, but in some respects he was outshone by his contemporary, Eli Whitney, a Yankee schoolteacher-turned-

AN AMPHIBIOUS DREDGE was America's first self-propelled wheeled vehicle. Built in Philadelphia in 1805 by a millwright, Oliver Evans, the steam-powered "mud machine" was secured to wooden axletrees and wheels for a trial run on dry land. After it had lumbered successfully through the city streets, Evans drove it to the water's edge and floated it off the underframe on an incoming tide.

engineer. Whitney devised sound and workable innovations for which the times were ready; they practically sold themselves, and their effect on society has been profound. Whitney is most famous for the invention of the cotton gin, which, by making large-scale, slave-worked plantations profitable, helped to bring about the Civil War. Less well known is his pioneering work in the mass production of mechanical devices from interchangeable parts, made to standard measurements by precision machine tools—a technique that is a foundation stone of modern industry.

This achievement, like those of many of the greatest engineers, is all the more notable because in retrospect it appears childishly simple. The idea of interchangeable parts now seems as logical as using a glass for drinking water. But in the early 1800s it was a wild departure from practice proved sound by thousands of years of experience with hand-crafted tools. Whitney's agreement to fill a government order for 10,000 Army muskets in the then incredibly short time of two years made him seem to be an addled eccentric. Whitney spent all of the first year devising the jigs and templates and special machinery for mass-producing the musket parts and setting them up in a production line in his Connecticut shop. He delivered only 500 muskets during those 12 months and in the end it took eight years instead of two to complete the contract. But when he finally went into production, grinding out parts by the thousands, he turned out three times as many muskets in a year as other gunsmiths could make working on one musket at a time. Whitney's unconventional procedure quickly became highly conventional.

Search for a practical pole

Like the concept of interchangeable parts, many solutions to engineering problems which seem easy after they succeed actually caused months and sometimes years of anguished frustration. The trolley pole, that backward-leaning, upward-pushing rod tipped with a grooved wheel which brought electric current from an overhead wire to the old streetcars, seems, by hindsight, to have been an easy arrangement to figure out. Yet when Frank Sprague was installing his first electrified streetcar system at Richmond, Virginia, in 1887, he tried 39 different types of trolley poles before he found the right one (originally conceived by Charles Van Depoele). With this solved, Sprague went on to become the principal figure in the development of American rapid transport.

Designing and perfecting the apparently trivial zipper, one of the most useful fastening devices ever developed, was anything but an easy job. As originally conceived by Whitcomb Judson in 1891, it was a hook-and-eye arrangement, sold under the name of C-Curity Placket Fastener. It was not, however, as secure as its name implied, because it had a disconcerting way of popping open and ripping garments. The company

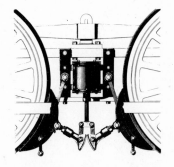

THE FIRST AIR BRAKES were developed during the 1860s by George Westinghouse, a young engineer who got the idea after reading about a compressed-air drill. The same principle produced railroad brakes so safe that the system is still in use. To set the brakes, an engineer pulls a lever which reduces the air pressure in a hose connecting all the cars. This reduction releases the valve of a pressurized air reservoir under each car (below), allowing air to flow into a brake cylinder between the wheels (above). Here the pressurized air forces down a piston, which sets a pair of brake shoes against the wheels. Any accident which breaks the air hose will thus stop the train automatically.

manufacturing the C-Curity fastener hired Gideon Sundback, a Swedish-born engineer, to try to remedy this fault. Sundback turned out several improved versions, but none was successful and the company was on the verge of failure. Then in 1913—22 years after Judson had begun work on the zipper idea—Sundback saved the business with a fastener of interlocking metal teeth, the prototype of the modern zipper.

On the other hand, problems that at first glance appear staggering as compared to designing a trolley pole or a practical zipper, have sometimes been solved quickly and with incredible simplicity. In 1848 Charles Ellet was faced with getting the first wire of a suspension bridge across the gorge below Niagara Falls. Before the iron-wire cable that was to support the bridge could be strung over the gorge, a catwalk for the workmen first had to be hung from shore to shore. In building such a catwalk for other suspension bridges, the initial wire had been towed across the water by boat or barge. But Ellet could not very well use a boat or barge to haul a wire across Niagara's churning, rock-strewn gorge.

A kite to build a bridge

The answer that Ellet came up with was as brilliant as it was simple. He offered five dollars to any local boy who could fly a kite across the gorge. A youngster named Homan Walsh collected the prize; his kite delivered a line of cord, attached to a wire-towing rope, to the opposite shore, and within a few weeks Ellet had a light service bridge a little more than seven feet wide suspended over the roaring canyon. Before railings were added to the bridge, Ellet, who combined showmanship with clever engineering, audaciously rode his horse across the swaying span, watched by a crowd of breathless spectators.

More sophisticated was the ingenuity that John Lucian Savage applied to a seemingly insurmountable obstacle during the building of Hoover Dam on the Colorado River in the 1930s. Savage, the chief designing engineer of this and other great American hydroelectric and irrigation projects, was up against a problem of literally monumental proportions. More than five million barrels of concrete was poured into the towering 726-foot wall of the dam—the greatest amount of concrete that had ever been used in a structure up to that time. But a heat-generating chemical reaction takes place when concrete sets, and the cooling and setting of such an enormous mass would ordinarily have taken 100 years. Savage could not wait for a century. He embedded more than 570 miles of pipes in the concrete, circulated cold river water through the pipes, and completed the cooling, shrinking and setting within two years. A variation of this idea was later used by Savage's engineers during a crisis in the construction of Grand Coulee Dam on the Columbia River in the state of Washington. A large section of clay in the wall of a steep embankment was threatening to slide, endangering the structure. The engineers ran pipes of chilling ammonia brine into the embankment and froze it solid.

A similar application of a familiar principle to a new use made possi-

PLAKO

The fastener that makes the skirt set perfectly

PLAKO is the C-Curity Fastener made perfect.

A PRIMITIVE ZIPPER, this slide fastener was based on a 19th Century invention by Whitcomb Judson, a self-educated engineer. It had two parallel rows of hooks and eyes which could be fastened and unfastened with a metal slide. But the first such fasteners often caused embarrassment, opening unexpectedly when the hooks popped out of the eyes. Not until engineers perfected its mechanism did the zipper become a reliable device *(opposite)*.

ble another valuable development. The principle was that of the lowly stapler; it was applied to save lives with delicate surgery. In response to a need for an instrument which could stitch together tiny nerves and blood vessels, Russian engineers made a stapler which fastens into place bits of tantalum-wire thread finer than a strand of human hair. The staples are so minute, in fact, that they must be loaded into the instrument under a magnifying glass. American surgeons found the stapler admirable but far too costly and complicated to be practical; hospital technicians needed two hours to disassemble it, clean it and reload it with staples after an operation. Then an engineering team composed of several specialists applied their ingenuity to an already ingenious tool. They redesigned and simplified the stapler. The improved instrument costs a fraction of its original price and can be cleaned and loaded quickly by ordinary operating-room personnel.

The ability to combine the new and the old, inventiveness, vision and a drive for simplicity and economy—all these attributes of the professional engineer were manifested recently in the work of a group of students at the University of Illinois. A classroom discussion of means by which astronauts might descend from space without injury was followed by an unusual assignment. The professor gave his students 12 class hours to design a protective package that would enable a raw egg to be catapulted 200 feet through the air and splash down without cracking its shell into a pool that graces the University Art Museum.

Twenty of the 24 students, using such cushioning devices as a wooden sphere filled with grease and a cocktail shaker lined with foam rubber and carpet padding, landed their eggs in the water unbroken. But the champion of the day was a student who surpassed the requirements— with showmanship. His missile blew itself apart in mid-air with a timed firecracker, releasing a parachute that gently lowered into the pool a capsule containing the egg packed in gelatin and peat moss. When the capsule touched the water, the moisture melted an aspirin tablet, switching on a tiny motor which propelled the uncracked egg proudly to shore.

From dreams to future realities

A classroom teaser, creatively solved, and nothing more? Perhaps. And yet imagination, the ability to envision the better way to solve the problems of his society, has always been a trait of the engineer. The engineer dreams, but he dreams of things that may someday be accomplished. When Othmar H. Ammann was designing his masterwork, the Verrazano-Narrows Bridge spanning the entrance to New York Harbor, he remarked sadly that in a way he was sorry to see it being built. For 50 years, he explained, engineers had been dreaming of putting such a suspension bridge—one of the world's longest—across the Narrows. Now they would no longer have that bridge to dream about. But when the Verrazano-Narrows Bridge, with its record-breaking central span of 4,260 feet, was nearing completion in 1964, engineers were already thinking about future suspension bridges with spans of 10,000 feet.

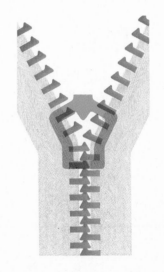

A FOOLPROOF ZIPPER like the one shown above was made possible in 1913 when a Swedish engineer, Gideon Sundback, got the idea of substituting tiny teeth *(below)* for Judson's hooks and eyes *(opposite)*. When a metal slide is pulled up, it first aligns the rows of teeth and then clamps them together, so that the tip of each tooth fits snugly into a notch on the tooth above and opposite it, interlocking them into a continuous fastening.

12,000 Engineers
to Make a Car

Many people still picture the engineer as a solitary, boot-shod adventurer armed with a transit, damming rivers and driving roads through the wilderness. The fact is that the great majority of engineers today work in teams—behind desks or in laboratories—tackling mutual problems with slide rules, computers and microscopes. The modern engineer fits no single mold. He is part scientist, part inventor, part technician, part cost accountant—and almost always a specialist in a narrow field. A metallurgical engineer may spend years improving industrial means for making tougher metal machine parts. A chemical engineer may do nothing but study better ways to manufacture quick-drying paints. Other engineers may focus on the design of highway interchanges or work assembly-line operations.

The skills of the Ford Motor Company's 12,000 engineers were culled and coordinated by an executive engineer when it was decided to build a completely new car, the Mustang. In its deployment of battalions of engineers, the automotive industry is typical; no modern industry could function without a similar array of diverse technological disciplines.

ENGINEERING A DREAM CAR
Executive engineer Roy Lunn *(center)* and some of his assistants examine a model of the Ford Mustang I, which they first conceived in 1962. The job of these engineers was to design a new model that included such features as rear-engine power, sports-car suspension and a low, rakish silhouette. Their work was the inspiration for the Mustang that went into mass production in 1964.

From Drawings to the First Hardware

The first step toward translating an engineering concept into reality is a drawing. A new car passes through scores of planning stages before it reaches this huge room, where hundreds of draftsmen make final drawings of every part of the body, from bumper to taillights.

With the help of a device called a coordinatograph *(left foreground)*, body engineers put together a three-dimensional, full-sized model of the car. They then start looking for bugs. The metal itself must be checked for quality *(below)*. Sometimes they find that a door will not swing freely or that the hood does not align with the grille. Changes must be made without delay: the body engineers have to process more than 100 models a year.

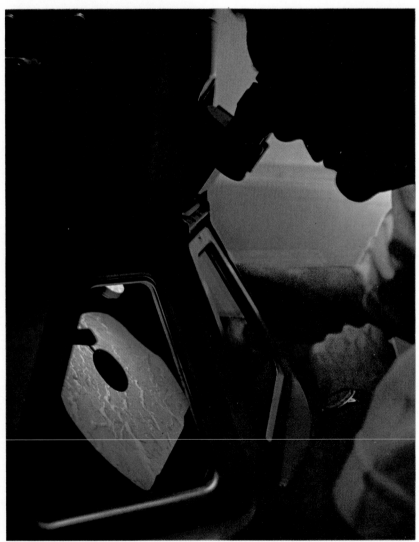

FROM TWO DIMENSIONS TO THREE
Precision drawings made by a corps of draftsmen *(left, background)* are scanned by the moving arm of a coordinatograph. A computer will convert the coordinatograph's diagram measurements into taped instructions for the modeling of three-dimensional body sections.

INSPECTING THE MATERIAL
Peering through the lens of an electron microscope, an instrumentation engineer examines the structure of steel to be used in cars. The arrangement of the crystals, which are magnified 10,000 times by the microscope, determines how easily the steel will bend or break.

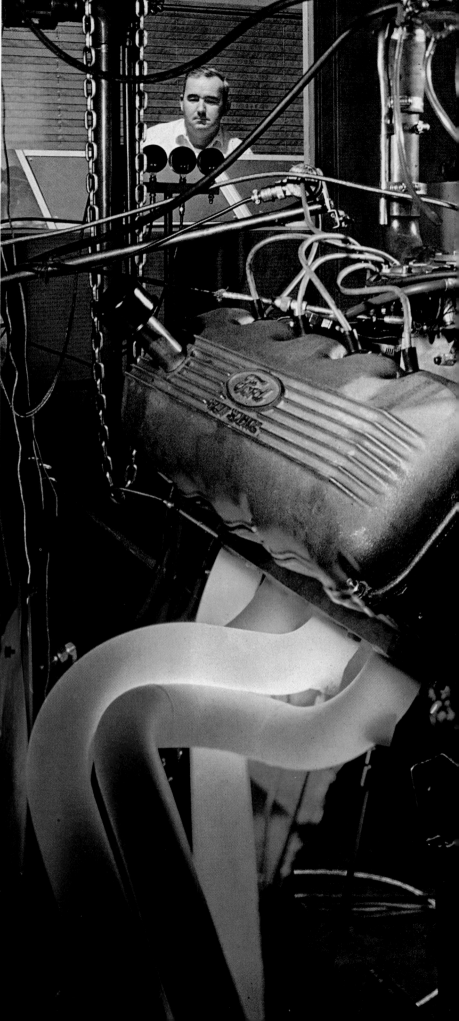

MORE POWER FOR A RACING CAR

Behind thick protective glass, an engineer scrutinizes a racing-car engine as it pits its 600 horsepower against a performance-measuring machine called a dynamometer. In these tests, engineers run the engines at abnormally high speeds to find the performance limits of such new parts as aluminum cylinder heads. Pressed to extremes, the engines sometimes fly apart.

TOUGHER PORCELAIN FOR A PLUG

In a test of a sparkplug insulator, an engineer shoots 30,000 volts of electricity across a porcelain cylinder. The test will indicate if the insulator is flawed, because the electricity will not arc from top to bottom, as shown, but through the side of the insulator. The special porcelain, developed to house a new type of sparkplug, was produced by a team of ceramics engineers.

Steady Gains
from Small Changes

The first Ford V-8 engine, produced in 1932, was a dramatic achievement of automotive engineering. Its design, which neatly fitted eight cylinders into a compact, lightweight V shape, made possible a considerable jump in performance with no significant rise in the price of the car.

The operating principles of a V-8 *(left)* have not changed since then. But engineers gradually raised its efficiency by subtle alterations—shortened piston stroke, higher compression and better ignition. The secret of such progress is a coordinated attack on details: a 50-man team may design carburetors, which are among the least efficient parts of an engine; only half as many work on cooling systems, which are considered about as good as they can be made.

Refinement goes beyond the sharpening of familiar tools. Automotive engineers are engaged in a major effort to build an economical gas turbine engine, expected to power long-haul trucks and buses by the mid-1970s. The vibration-free turbine is, in effect, a many-bladed fan spun 37,500 times a minute by hot gases. But the expense of building components that can withstand flaming gases at 2,000° F., makes turbines practical only for trucks at present.

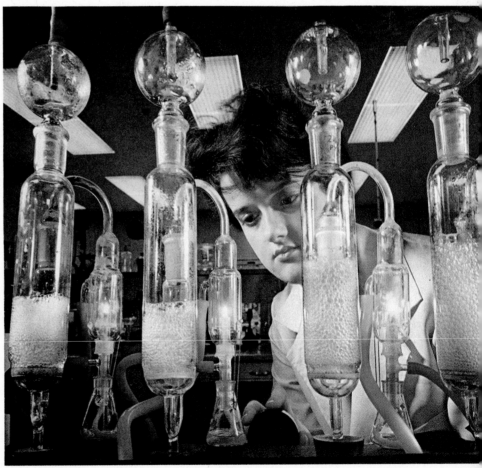

FUEL CHECK IN THE LAB
Janet Mackie, one of the few women engineers in the automotive industry, measures the sulfur content of various fuels. Since sulfur is a corrosive agent, tests are made periodically to determine the damage fuels might do to engine metals. Ford chemical engineers also are developing better body paints, engine oils, and lubricants for the suspension and the bearings.

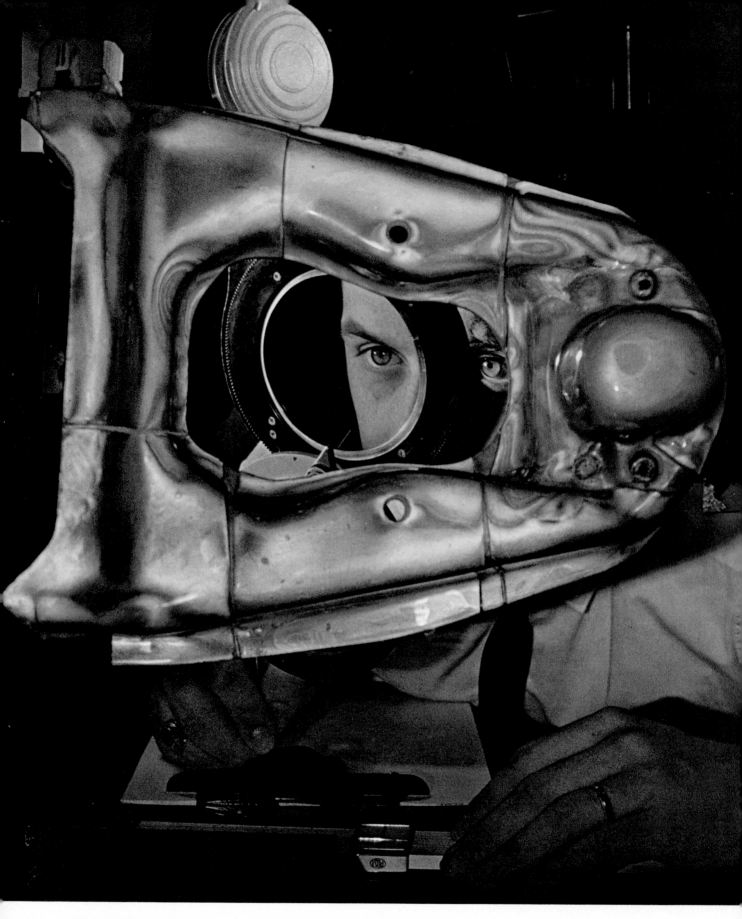

VISIBLE SIGNS OF STRAIN

Under polarized light, the strained areas of a suspension part are visually identified by a test engineer. The part, called an upper control arm, cradles a front wheel. It has been coated with a plastic that shows swirls of rainbow colors when the control arm is twisted. The greatest stress occurs where the color lines are closest together. If the metal is not thick enough in these areas, engineers will order a new design.

Torturing Parts for Reliability

Engineers try to design a car like the poet's Wonderful One Hoss Shay, which worked perfectly until one day every single part wore out at the same instant. Automotive engineers aim at a reliable life of 100,000 miles for the 12,000 basic parts in a car.

After a part is designed by an engineer, it is run through an ordeal of twisting, vibrating, and sub-zero temperatures. Hundreds of machines test reliability—cranking windows, slamming doors, bouncing springs until the part breaks. In one chassis test *(left)*, engineers can glimpse exact patterns of stress. A part that breaks early requires a new design. A part that lasts far longer than the others also returns to the drawing board. Engineers can make it a little weaker—as long as it matches the lifetime of the rest of the car—and the buyer gets the benefit of economy.

A SUPERRELIABLE CHASSIS

An engineer adjusts holes for dashboard instruments on a racing-car chassis made of honeycomb aluminum. This lightweight material, full of air spaces, is remarkably strong and resistant to metal fatigue. The slightest flaw could be disastrous, since the chassis is destined for a Grand Prix car that will compete in 24-hour races and hit speeds over 200 miles per hour.

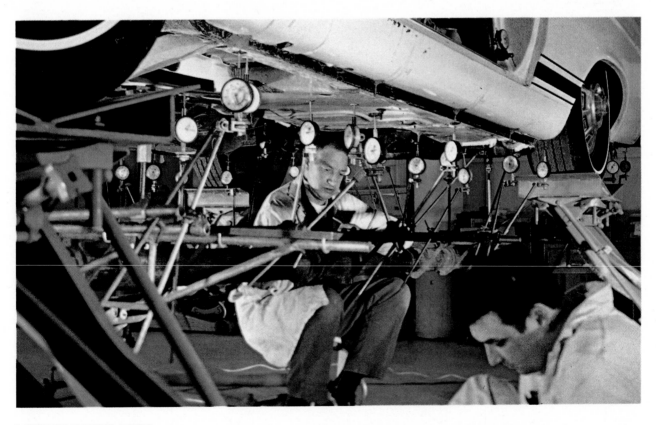

A TEST OF CHASSIS-AGING

To detect signs of metal fatigue, test engineers take readings from indicators on a test-car chassis that is being twisted lengthwise. The car has been driven 10,000 miles over rough roads. It will be returned to the test track for more punishment, and then the chassis will be rechecked. In this manner, engineers can catalogue wear and tear on a chassis as it passes through an average lifetime of 100,000 miles.

AN ENGINEER WHO THINKS SMALL

An electrical engineer peers through a lens at a wafer of microcircuitry *(above)* that may soon replace the complicated ignition-system circuits shown under the soldering gun below. Developed by the electronics industry, these ignition microcircuits are made of thin layers of silicon crystals upon which the components are etched. Similar microcircuits may be used in miniaturized computers for car-guidance systems that could serve as autopilots; the computer would steer the vehicle and operate the accelerator while the driver merely watches.

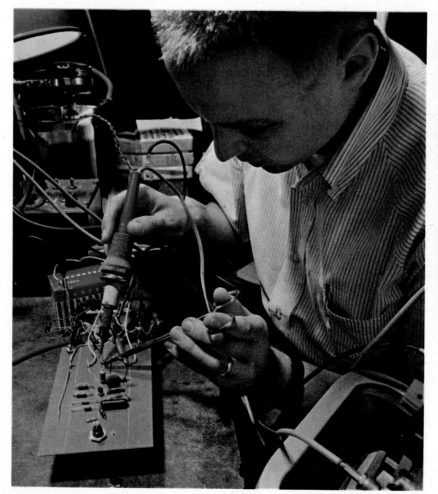

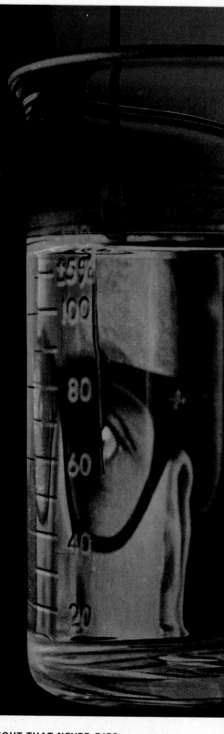

A LIGHT THAT NEVER DIES

A light as cold and nonglaring as the glow of a firefly is created by a chemical engineer who is working with physicists to develop an illumination source that will not deteriorate from heat. The cool light is produced when current is run through crystals in an electrolyte solution.

Engineering's Advance Guard

Engineers are always looking for the better way. The automobile of 65 years ago—the engineering marvel of the age—was started up with a hand crank that could kick like a mule; it was steered by a boat tiller; the driver poked a stick into the gas tank to check his fuel; the dashboard had not a single instrument.

Today, more than 1,000 Ford engineers are researching such futuristic car components as fingernail-sized ignition systems *(left)*, steering that is electronically locked onto cables buried in the road, and durable headlights or interior lights *(above)* that shine with the soft, cold glow of a firefly. Only two decades from now, present cars may seem as primitive as the flivvers of 1906 seem today.

In a high-speed photographic sequence, a 1965 Ford Thunderbird approaches a concrete barrier at 30 mph to test the effect of the impact

safety belt. During the crash, the crumpling of metal absorbs some of the impact energy, but the dummies in the rear seat slam forward and

Students of a Driver's Nightmare

When the first cars came along, some people noted that they did not shy or buck like a horse and concluded that an era of safe travel had arrived. By 1970 motor accidents were killing over 55,000 Americans a year. Recently, a new breed of engineers—safety specialists working in government agencies, universities and the auto industry—has arisen to combat this appalling death toll. Much of this work aims at safer car designs, better roads and traffic control, and improved driver education and testing.

Some safety engineers study the moment of horror itself—the fractions of a second when human bodies make contact with the hard interior surfaces of a crashing automobile. Recording events with movie cameras, they run cars head on into walls and roll them over at high speeds. In certain university experiments, human cadavers are used to find how much pressure a body can bear when it is wrenched by a seat belt or thrust against a steering wheel. Another university safety study sends doctors to the scenes of actual accidents for a closeup view.

Spurred by the National Highway Safety Bureau, engineers are guiding the designs for such devices as inflatable front-seat air bags, collapsible steering wheels and more effective seat belts. Their job is crucial: in terms of human lives, cars are the world's most dangerous machines.

26

on its "passengers." The occupants actually are dummies—two in the rear, and one in the front seat harnessed in an experimental ceiling-hung

then hit the floor. The shoulder belt of the front "passenger" holds during the crucial ninety thousandths of a second after the instant of impact.

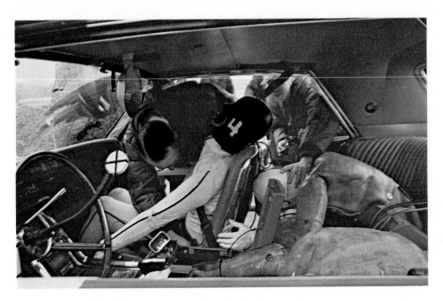

THE AFTERMATH

The "passenger" in the death seat—so called because the right front seat is the most dangerous of all—would have lived through the wreck shown above. Shoulder belts like the one on the dummy have been required for two front-seat occupants since January 1, 1968.

A FLOW CHART FOR THE PLANT

Facing an intricate chart of the flow of car parts within a Mustang assembly plant, an engineer studies a change in production-line layout to prepare for the next year's models. Manufacturing engineers utilize the mathematics of statistics to help them organize a multitude of operations and to predict the likelihood of breakdown or error at widely scattered points.

THE RIVER OF PRODUCTION

Hot sparks from a welder shower over the body build-up line as workers piece together Mustang parts which are brought by a feeder line *(above, right)*. During the early stages of production, there are three separate lines for assembly of the body, engine and chassis. Mustang bodies are joined to chassis before the engines are added—though many manufacturing engineers prefer to put the engine on the chassis before the body arrives. When a car reaches the end of the assembly line, a worker steps in and drives the car off under its own power.

Organizing Men and Machines

Manufacturing engineers, responsible for mass-producing a product, have a profound respect for the power of numbers. In Ford's U.S. plants it is their task to organize the actions of 50,000 workers so that about three million vehicles a year are put together in the most efficient manner.

The speed of automobile assembly is as formidable as the volume: a car can be put together in one and a half days; in an average plant, 700 cars are in the system at the same time; feeder lines must bring the correct fender, radio or gearshift lever to the right worker at precisely the right time. The entire operation is coordinated by a computer, but it is the manufacturing engineers who program the computer and dictate which car parts should be installed first.

Over a year's time a tiny bottleneck can cost thousands of dollars. Thus, if the engineers see that a worker cannot bolt on an exhaust system in an allotted time, they will divide the operation into two or more stages. To make certain they are bringing men and machines together in the cheapest, fastest order, Ford's manufacturing engineers use a pilot plant to design and test out the assembly process down to the smallest detail.

MASS-PRODUCING CUSTOM CARS
An assortment of Mustangs nears the end of the assembly process. Each of these cars is being built to meet a specific order from a dealer or customer—who may choose from among more than 150,000 combinations of colors, accessories and optional equipment. The customer's order, recorded on a punched card, is fed into a computer. By teletyped instructions, the computer controls the movement of the proper parts along feeder lines throughout the plant. The time between the receipt of the order and delivery of the car to a dealer averages 16 days.

After two years of engineering effort, thousands of Mustangs go out to dealers from a factory in Dearborn, Michigan. By this time the engineers

who created these cars—experts in design, metals, plastics, electricity, quality control and assembly tools—have already turned to new models.

2
The "Old Man" and His Helpers

A self-educated 18th Century engineer, James Brindley began his career as a mill-wright. Although he was considered an inept apprentice by his master, he went on to win lasting fame as the builder of a network of shipping canals in England.

CROSSING THE ATLANTIC in his younger days as a mining engineer, Herbert Hoover shared a dining table and much convivial conversation with a cultivated English lady. "We were coming up New York Harbor at the final farewell breakfast," wrote Hoover in his memoirs, "when she turned to me and said: 'I hope you will forgive my dreadful curiosity but I should like awfully to know—what is your profession?'" Hoover said he was an engineer. The English lady drew back, shocked, and exclaimed, "Why, I thought you were a gentleman!"

Her remark reflected an attitude that prevailed in Britain and America until late in the 19th Century—an attitude that seems as strange to us today as it would have been to the ancient Egyptians, who esteemed the engineers responsible for their monumental edifices and public works. In our own time, there is scarcely any position of eminence beyond the engineer's reach: Herbert Hoover, of course, became President of the United States.

The explanation for the engineer's rise to prestige lies in the progressive changes that have occurred in the way he works. Most of the men who pioneered engineering in the mid-18th Century were skilled but uneducated craftsmen who tackled difficult technological problems armed with little more than ingenuity and energy. As their empirical knowledge accumulated, it became available to a later generation of engineers in handbooks and, gradually, in textbooks. But it was the increasingly complex world of the late 19th Century, with its increasingly sophisticated technology, that brought about the greatest change. In particular, the growing use of electricity, which obeys none of the old "common sense" rules, heralded the end of the old rule-of-thumb engineer and hastened the evolution of the modern, science-oriented professional man. Intuition, empirical knowledge and handbooks were still important elements in successful engineering, but they were no longer enough. The new engineer needed a broader education, embracing science, mathematics, economics and even politics. And with professional training came prestige.

During the Industrial Revolution that transformed England from an agricultural country into the most powerful industrial nation in the world, the gigantic task of building canals, roads, bridges, railroads, factories and foundries was accomplished—superbly—by self-taught men. Thomas Newcomen and James Watt, whose steam engines started the Revolution, were both unschooled mechanics. Thomas Telford, the great road and bridge builder, started as a stonemason. Richard Trevithick was a wrestler and strong man before he built the first steam engine to run on wheels, thus fathering Britain's railways.

Engineering work in those Georgian and Victorian times, and in the earlier days of the Mesopotamians, Egyptians, Greeks and Romans, can best be described by picturing The Old Man and his helpers—the boss in charge of the project, assisted by a crew of expert foremen who carried out his orders. It was always a one-man show, whether the Old Man was Khufu-onekh of Egypt raising the Great Pyramid around 2600

B.C., or George Henry Corliss assembling his giant, 1,400-horsepower steam engine at the Philadelphia Centennial Exhibition in 1876. The Old Man called every move, made every decision, tolerated no interference; he took the credit when the job was done or the blame if it was not. Queen Victoria's consort, Prince Albert, was reported to have said of the Old Man of his era, "If we want any work done of an unusual character, and send for an architect, he hesitates, debates, trifles; we send for an engineer, and he *does it.*"

The Old Men who worked out solutions for brand-new problems at the beginning of the Industrial Revolution had few precedents to guide them, but they had plenty of common sense. One such pragmatic engineer, and a remarkably successful one, was the canal builder James Brindley.

Carrying coal to Manchester

There were no long inland canals in England in 1759 when the Duke of Bridgewater hired Brindley to build one to convey coal from the Duke's mine at Worsley to the manufacturing town of Manchester, 10 miles away. The roads were then so bad that coal and other goods had to be laboriously transported on pack horses. In his travels, the Duke had seen the Grand Canal of Languedoc, which had been constructed 100 years earlier in southeastern France to connect the Atlantic with the Mediterranean. It had struck him that a similar waterway would solve his coal-transportation difficulties.

His engineer, Brindley, had never seen a shipping canal and knew nothing about canal construction except what the Duke told him of the Grand Canal. When he went to work for the Duke, he was a simple country fellow, a mill mechanic with a local reputation for figuring out remedies for any kind of technical problem.

Surveying the countryside between the Duke's mine and Manchester, Brindley made two resolutions about canal building before he turned a shovelful of earth: he would not join his waterway to a river or brook for fear of trouble in the flood season, and he would keep his canal flat, to avoid locks to higher or lower ground. He likened water to a giant: "If you lay the giant flat upon his back, he loses all his force," Brindley said. But to get to Manchester, the canal had to cross the Irwell River and its steep valley.

Brindley's approach to the problem, which the Duke accepted with delight and admiration, led most Englishmen of the time, including other engineers, to suspect that both men were demented. Brindley proposed to carry the canal across the river and valley on an aqueduct bridge of arched stone, 200 yards long, 12 yards wide and 39 feet high. Thus he could maintain the canal on a level course and eliminate the locks that would have been required to lower the barges to the river and lift them back to canal level on the opposite side of the valley. Aqueducts, of course, were no novelty; the Romans had constructed them 20 centuries before to supply water to their cities. But no one in

England had ever heard of using one as an elevated bridge for shipping.

Despite scoffers, Brindley had his way, as Old Men usually did. When the canal was opened to traffic in 1761, the span over the river—called the Barton Aqueduct—was hailed as the wonder of the age. The sight of coal barges being towed by horses and mules along a waterway "hung in the air" while boats passed under them on the river below stirred one contemporary lady writer to praise the project as "perhaps the greatest artificial curiosity in the world." She added, "Crowds of people, including those of the first fashion, resort to it daily."

In building his canal, Brindley met a multitude of other problems with amazing sophistication. Instead of ending the waterway at the mouth of the Duke's mine, he extended it underground into the mine itself. Barges could then be loaded where the coal was dug; at the same time the canal drained seepage from the mine. At the canal's Manchester terminal, the Duke had planned to unload the coal on a dock at the foot of a steep hill; buyers would have had to haul it in carts and wheelbarrows to a road on top of the hill. Such an inefficient setup offended Brindley's taste. He dug a tunnel bringing the canal into the hillside and drove a shaft down from the top of the hill to meet it. Coal was hoisted from the barges up through the shaft by a crane, which was powered by a waterwheel harnessing a nearby waterfall.

Puddled clay for waterways

Less sophisticated than these accomplishments but just as efficient was Brindley's method of lining his canal with puddled clay to make it leakproof. This substance, a mixture of clay, water and sand, became impervious to water when kneaded or chopped with spades. On an occasion when he was questioned about puddling, Brindley tried to explain the process but gave up and asked for a lump of raw clay. He shaped this into a trough and poured water into it. The water immediately began to seep through the clay. Then he kneaded the clay with sand and water, shaped it once again into a trough and filled it with liquid. This time the trough did not leak. "Thus it is," Brindley said, "that I form a water-tight trunk to carry water over rivers and valleys, whenever they cross the path of the canal."

After completing the Bridgewater canal, the Duke and Brindley extended it 23 miles westward to the salt tidewater of the Mersey, thus linking Manchester and Liverpool by inland navigation. For this project Brindley not only directed a gang of 600 workmen, but also arranged to have barges, fitted as blacksmith, carpentry and masonry shops, move along with the construction site as it inched slowly forward. He bought land rights from farmers, handled the payroll and kept account of wood cut for piles and bulkheads and gravel dug for embankments. He managed to keep the canal route level all the way to the shore of the Mersey, where the barges were to take to the open tidewater for the remaining few miles to Liverpool. But at Runcorn a 79-foot drop to the Mersey's low-tide mark forced him to use locks for the first time. The finished canal, by supplying coal from the Worsley mine to Manchester's steam engines at half the previous price, and by providing direct and efficient access to the ocean shipping docks of Liverpool, made Manchester the manufacturing center of the new industrial England.

But even that was not Brindley's masterwork. His greatest project, which was not finished until after his death in 1772, was the Grand Trunk Canal, 140 miles long and requiring 75 locks, five tunnels, 160 aqueducts and 109 highway bridges. Connecting the Bridgewater canal system with the Trent and Severn Rivers, it was the main stem of a network that provided England with inland waterways between its east and west coasts, linking the ports of Liverpool, Bristol and Hull to inland districts producing pottery, coal and salt.

Footwork in a tunnel

The Grand Trunk Canal took 11 years to complete; construction was delayed by a tunnel one and two thirds miles long which had to be dug through a mountain at Harecastle. To save labor, time and expense, Brindley made the tunnel only 12 feet high and nine feet wide, with no towpath for horses or mules; bargemen had to stow their animals aboard, lie on their backs and propel barges through the tunnel by pushing with their feet against the ceiling. A Staffordshire man who saw the tunnel during construction invited a friend to "come to view our eighth wonder of the world, the subterraneous navigation, which is cutting by Mr. Brindley, who handles rocks as easily as you would plum-pies, and makes the four elements subservient to his will. He is as plain a looking man as one of the boors of the Peak or as one of his own carters; but when he speaks, all ears listen, and every mind is filled with wonder at the things he pronounces to be practicable."

In planning his engineering feats, Brindley never worked with drawings or models. Once, when asked what the arches of a proposed canal aqueduct would look like, he sent to a market for a cheese, sliced it in halves, placed the two semicircular portions on a table with their round sides up and laid a ruler across their tops to represent the trough of the canal. With no engineering handbooks or expert advisers to turn to and relying solely on his own intuition and original thinking, Brindley would take a hard problem to bed with him and stay there, thinking, sometimes for several days, until he worked out a solution. His brother-in-law wrote: "He would then get up and execute his design. . . . His memory was so remarkable that he often declared that he could remember, and execute, all parts of the most complex machine, provided he had time, in his survey of it, to settle in his mind the several parts and their relations to each other. His method of calculating the powers of any machine invented by him was peculiar to himself. He worked the question for

A CONTROVERSIAL AQUEDUCT, designed by James Brindley and built in 1761, carried an early English canal across the Irwell River. Other engineers had claimed that such "a river hung in air" could never be built. But a thick lining of puddled clay—an impervious mixture of sand and clay—kept the aqueduct watertight. Legend has it that Brindley was so worried that something might go wrong that he stayed in bed the day the canal was opened, refusing to come out until he heard that the project had been a success.

some time in his head and then put down the results in figures. After this, taking it up again at that stage, he worked it again in his mind for a certain time and set down the results as before. In the same way he still proceeded, making use of figures only at stated parts of the question. Yet the ultimate result was generally true, though the road he travelled in search of it was unknown to all but himself and perhaps it would not have been in his power to show it to another."

Original thinking like James Brindley's continued to be the outstanding strength of successful Old Men in later generations. But with the advance of the Industrial Revolution, this strength became reinforced by an ever-widening store of empirical knowledge and technological know-how. Engineers now began to benefit from the hard-earned workshop experience gained by their predecessors.

George Stephenson, for instance, working on the first practical coal-hauling locomotive at the Killingworth Colliery in northeastern England in 1814, was not groping with such unknown quantities as Brindley had faced when he planned the Duke of Bridgewater's canal in 1759. Stephenson had the experiences of Watt, Oliver Evans, Richard Trevithick and other earlier steam-power experimenters to guide him.

Like the intuitive engineers, the empirical Old Men of 19th Century Britain and America had no handbooks and little fundamental knowledge of the principles of nature. They did, however, possess imagination and the drive to turn the fruit of their imagination into reality.

Building machines by trial-and-error

John Fritz was such a man. He was a farm boy who left school in 1838 at the age of 16 to work in a rural machine-repair shop, and then rose to become the leading iron and steel engineer of the United States. In the 1860s, when Fritz was chief engineer for the Bethlehem Iron Company in Pennsylvania, he would dispense with written specifications and instead make chalk sketches for mechanical parts on the pattern-room floor, or simply tell someone what he needed. "Time and again," one of Fritz's associates said, "he would not know just what he wanted until after the pattern or model was made and he was able to see the shape of the piece he was designing." When a new machine was assembled, Fritz would say to his workers, "Now, boys, we have got her done—let's start her up and see why she doesn't work." The Old Men of Fritz's day expected the first machine to fail; by studying its defects, they would then succeed on the second or third try. Using such trial-and-error methods, Fritz built at Bethlehem in 1873 one of America's first Bessemer steel plants. With the Bessemer process, steel, once a luxury, was made widely available for rails and buildings.

In the tradition of all famous Old Men, when Fritz formed an opinion on an engineering matter, nothing could change it. At the time that he was trying out the Siemens-Martin open-hearth system, which produced a finer grade of steel than the Bessemer process, Fritz made a deal with the Siemens-Martin representative to install one of that company's regenerative gas furnaces at Bethlehem. Fritz mentioned that he thought the furnace's roof was too low to allow proper combustion. The Siemens-Martin representative, a Mr. Leach, asked him if he pretended to know more than Dr. Siemens, who had developed the furnace.

"I told him that I had puddled and heated more iron than Dr. Siemens had," Fritz wrote in his autobiography, "and had more experience in rolling mill practice where great heat was required; but Mr. Leach was not willing to let me make any changes in the construction. We compromised on a straight roof, but I didn't build it, as I knew it wasn't right. When we came to build the furnace I built it just as I wanted it, and it was eminently successful."

The handbook engineers

By the mid-19th Century newly founded engineering schools began turning out their first graduates—the engineers who had studied some mathematics and physics and who replaced rule-of-thumb experiments with exact procedure and tested facts. Their approach to a problem was to gather as much published data about it as possible, evaluate the data carefully and then select a course of action. Very often the intensive examination of data led to a highly original solution.

Frederick W. Taylor, the peppery little efficiency man, was one of the most imaginative of the handbook engineers. Before he introduced his famed scientific management theories to speed industrial production, timing hand laborers with a stopwatch, Taylor studied mechanical engineering at Stevens Institute of Technology. He became a devout advocate of precise data-collecting while he was improving manufacturing methods at the Midvale Steel Company in Philadelphia, where he worked as chief engineer in the 1890s. Taylor once told how he had gone about designing a new type of steam hammer at Midvale, referring to himself modestly in the third person:

"This machine was of such a nature that it battered itself to pieces. Almost all of its parts broke. There was a young engineer who had many of these machines in his manufacturing department and who decided to build a machine that would not batter itself to pieces. He spent one or two years in collecting, from all over the world, data about various similar machines until he found instances in which some one of the parts of each of the various machines of different designs had never broken. He then copied the design of each of the parts which had not been broken, collecting one element from one machine, another from another, a third from a third, etc. There was, however, one portion of the machine of which he could find no single instance of a design which had not, at some time or another, broken. He devoted his special energy and ingenuity to the study of this element and finally evolved what he believed

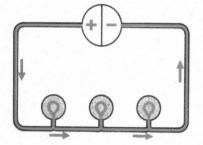

THE SERIES CIRCUIT *(above)*, still used in strings of Christmas-tree bulbs, was the only type in general use in 1878, when Thomas Edison began developing a distribution system for his bulb. But the series circuit has a serious flaw: when one bulb is disconnected or burns out, the entire circuit *(color)* is broken and all the other bulbs go out. To overcome this problem, Edison used a parallel circuit *(below)* —in which each bulb draws electricity independently from its own copper wire —for his first lighting demonstrations.

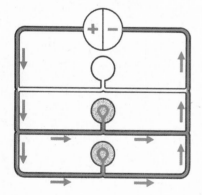

would be a principle which would prevent it from breaking. He then constructed a machine containing all of the parts already existing which had not broken, plus one of his own design and patent which he believed would not break, and as a result obtained a machine which lasted for many years without a single breakdown—the first instance of its kind in the history of that art."

Taylor's meticulous procedure may seem to have been a drastic departure from the casual approach of John Fritz, but handbook engineering and empirical engineering had a basic similarity: both were founded on evaluation of past experience.

Yet even experience is not always an infallible guide. With the rise of electrical engineering, which dealt with a new and intangible form of energy not covered by any facts tabulated in the handbooks, technology became so complex that an entirely new approach was called for. Intuition and handbooks were not enough. Electrical engineers needed scientific knowledge, mathematics and sophisticated approaches—and so did other engineers of the new era.

Perhaps the greatest of all the Old Men was Thomas Alva Edison. And no one better illustrates the changeover in engineering. In 1883 he began installing one of the first overhead electrical distribution networks, in Sunbury, Pennsylvania. One of the problems in lighting the village was to determine the proper diameter of the copper wire for the system's feeders and branches. If the wire were not thick enough, the customers' lights would be too dim; if it were thicker than the current load required, the wire's cost would skyrocket.

Edison attacked the problem empirically: he built a small-scale model of Sunbury's whole distribution system, with a peg representing each subscriber's home. Each peg was wound with resistance wire, the number of turns on the peg corresponding to the number of lamps in that house. Tiny branch-line feeders were strung along the model's streets, leading to the heavier main wires attached to the model's powerhouse. When the model was completed, a task that took a crew of men several days, the current was turned on and its strength was measured with various sizes of wire, until a wire of the proper thickness was found.

Dawn of a new era

One of Edison's engineers at the time was young Frank Sprague, an Annapolis graduate who was later to play a leading role in the development of subway and trolley car transportation for American cities. He was appalled by this rigamarole. With pencil and paper he worked out a set of mathematical formulas to calculate ideal wire gauges for varying lengths and loads. Then he showed Edison how the proper size of wire for the Sunbury installation could be estimated in a single afternoon. Sprague's calculations worked perfectly, convincing the Wizard of Menlo Park—as the rest of the Old Men were already learning—that scientific analysis could be quicker, easier and more exact than trial-and-error engineering. The age of the Old Man was over.

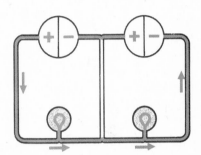

THE THREE-WIRE CIRCUIT, the basis of modern electrical distribution systems, was invented by Thomas Edison in 1882 to save expensive copper wire in his first community electrification project, at Sunbury, Pennsylvania. By placing two circuits together, he made three wires perform the work of four. The middle, or neutral, wire carries no current when the load on both circuits is equal *(above).* But whenever the load is unequal *(below),* current instantly flows through the middle wire to maintain a balanced circuit.

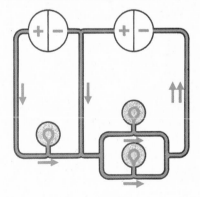

The Wizard of Menlo Park

Thomas Alva Edison, inventor of the incandescent light bulb, the phonograph, motion pictures and literally hundreds of other devices ranging from stock tickers to ore separators, is a unique figure in the history of engineering. With only three months of formal schooling (his teacher called him "addled"), Edison was the last and greatest of the old-time tinkerer-inventors. Scoffing at "ivory tower" theoretical scientists, he tackled the uncharted realm of electricity with intuition, imagination and endless experimentation. "Genius," he later said, "is ninety-nine per cent perspiration and one per cent inspiration."

Nevertheless, Edison's career marks the transition of engineering from the jack-of-all-trades approach of such men as Eli Whitney, James Watt and Robert Fulton, to the science-oriented team efforts of today. As the director of groups of specialists in his New Jersey "invention factories" (first at Menlo Park and then at West Orange) Edison was, in effect, the prototype of the modern systems engineer. For he invented not only a successful incandescent light bulb, but an entire electrical system to go with it—362 patents in all.

AN INVENTOR'S SANCTUM
Edison's library, which doubled as his study and office, is now part of a museum in West Orange, New Jersey. The inventor's bust overlooks his desk, cluttered with notebooks and chemicals, and illuminated by a turn-of-the-century Edison bulb. The large photograph above the desk shows him after a marathon 72-hour session in 1888 during which he vastly improved the phonograph.

"I Have Got So Much to Do"

Edison had a restless, inquiring mind from the start; once, as a small boy, he sat for hours trying to hatch some goose and chicken eggs. He became an itinerant telegrapher at the age of 16, and within two years was sending and receiving Morse code flawlessly at an expert's rate of better than 45 words per minute.

All his spare time—and earnings—were devoted to his experiments. His prolific mind and skilled hands produced the automatic telegraph, which could handle 200 words per minute; the quadruplex, capable of sending and receiving up to four messages on a single line; and the even more versatile multiplex (right).

When Edison earned $40,000 from Western Union in 1870 for the first reliable stock ticker, he went into a profitable business in Newark, making stock tickers and electrical instruments. But he longed for more time to spend on his beloved experiments. He stated his goal when he was only 21: "I have got so much to do and life is so short, I am going to hustle."

ENGINEERS FOR HIRE
In 1869 Edison and a friend, Franklin Pope, offered their services as electrical engineers, a virtually unheard-of specialty. But Edison quit within a year because he felt he was not getting enough money. Instead he got a job as an inventor and troubleshooter for Western Union.

A SUCCESSFUL STOCK TICKER

Offered $40,000 for his third patent, the Universal stock ticker *(above)*, Edison felt "as near fainting as I ever got." His first patented invention, a vote recorder to eliminate voice voting in Congress, was rejected. According to one Congressman, it "would destroy the only hope that the minority would have of influencing legislation." Edison then resolved to invent only products that were certain of commercial success.

THE PEN AND THE MULTIPLEX

Edison's electric pen *(above)*, which he invented in 1874, was a forerunner of the modern mimeograph machines. Powered by wet-cell batteries *(colored liquids)*, it had a vibrating stylus that perforated holes in a stencil, from which copies could be made. At left, in front of a collection of mementos from Edison's youth, is a model of his ingenious multiplex telegraph, invented in 1876. The portrait shows him at 16.

The Menlo Park Invention Factory

In 1876 Edison moved from Newark to Menlo Park, New Jersey, where he soon gathered a handful of skilled young assistants and a dozen or so mechanics and did nothing but work on inventions. By stressing systematic research, Edison turned his new setup into a pioneering "invention factory"—the prototype of modern engineering laboratories. Edison's goal, "a minor invention every ten days and a big thing every six months or so," was amply realized. By 1887, when he left Menlo Park, his list of nearly 400 patents included the electric light and phonograph.

But in the opinion of some engineers Edison's greatest invention was his organized assault on every aspect of a problem—such as the creation of the generators, fuses, conduits and other equipment that made his light bulb a practical contribution rather than merely an interesting novelty.

A HISTORIC LABORATORY
Edison's Menlo Park laboratory is reconstructed as part of a museum in Dearborn, Michigan. The framed photograph shows the laboratory as it appeared in 1880, with the 15-man team that was then working on the electric light. Edison is seated in the center, facing front.

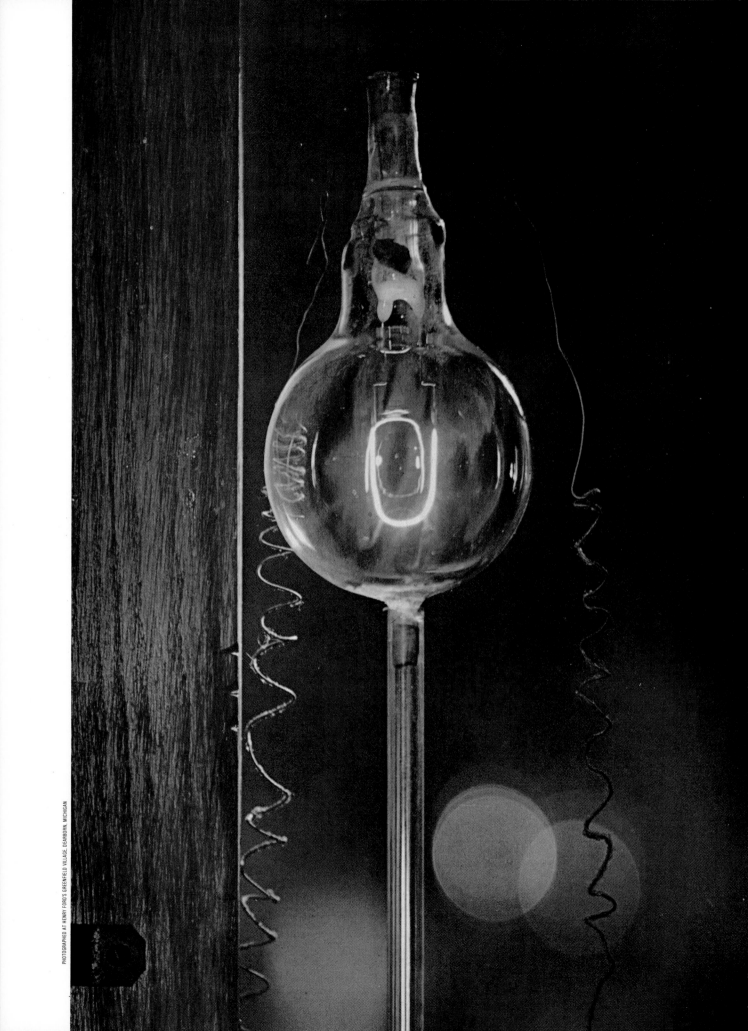

To Build
a Better Bulb

Various inventors had been working for years to perfect an incandescent light bulb before Edison began to think about the problem in 1877. But after studying every bit of information on these projects—all of which used thick, low-resistance filaments requiring a high current—Edison became convinced that his rivals were on the wrong track. He put his Menlo Park team to work on a new approach and in 1879 patented the first successful bulb, built around a thin, high-resistance filament of carbonized thread.

The first few bulbs glowed beautifully, but their filaments generally burned out within 40 hours. Setting out to find a better filament, Edison and his staff launched a lengthy search for the elusive substance. "Somewhere in God's mighty workshop," he declared, "there is a dense woody growth, with fibers almost geometrically parallel . . . from which we can make the filament the world needs." He systematically tested and rejected thousands of materials until one day in 1880, as he was toying with a fan, he peeled off a strip of bamboo, examined it under a microscope and then tested it in a bulb. The search was over. Here was a satisfactory filament, one that figured to burn for at least 600 hours. The new bulb was a commercial success, and Edison now could concentrate on extending his integrated power and lighting system into the homes, offices and factories of the United States.

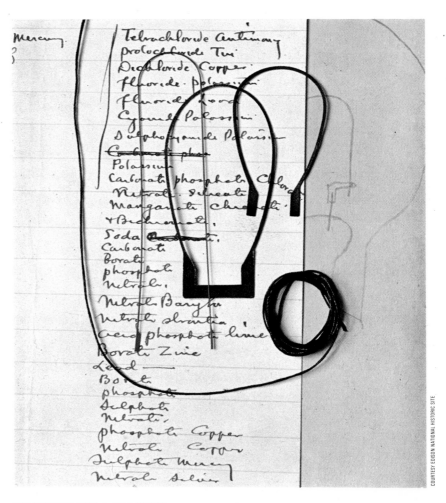

SEARCHING FOR A FILAMENT
Three types of carbonized filament material that were actually used—cotton thread, bamboo and cardboard—lie atop Edison's handwritten list of some of the 7,600 fibers and minerals tested as filaments or coatings. Tungsten, the present filament substance, was not tested because, until 1904, nobody had learned how to process the brittle metal into the proper shape.

"LET THERE BE LIGHT"
A replica of the first successful light bulb glows triumphantly in a reenactment of the historic event of October 21, 1879. Edison made this bulb exactly half a century later, for the Golden Jubilee of Light. As he connected the wires to turn it on, he said, "Let there be light!"

THE SAFETY FACTOR
Edison's safety fuses made his lights safe and practical for home use. An early fuse saved one of his first lighting demonstrations from disaster when a gas company official deliberately short-circuited a connection. Only four of the bulbs went out, and the culprit was ejected.

The First Lighting System

In 1879, Edison's lighting system, employing 53 bulbs, was successfully demonstrated in Menlo Park. By 1882 a more advanced system was installed in Lower Manhattan, supplying electricity to an area of about a quarter of a square mile.

But it soon became evident that the system contained a built-in limitation: its direct current, produced at low, safe voltages, was ineffective if carried over two miles. In 1885, George Westinghouse and William Stanley developed a practical alternating-current transformer, which enabled higher voltages to be transmitted cheaply over long distances. But Edison stubbornly refused to convert. He did not admit his error until 20 years later, when he said to Stanley's son, "Tell your father I was wrong."

THE SOURCE OF A SYSTEM
An Edison-designed generator like the one above —nicknamed a "long-waisted Mary Ann"— powered the first incandescent lighting system. Driven by a steam engine, it converted 90 per cent of its mechanical energy into electricity— an efficiency rating equal to modern generators.

PHOTOGRAPHED AT HENRY FORD'S GREENFIELD VILLAGE, DEARBORN, MICHIGAN

The first demonstration of Edison's lighting system, here restaged in the

Menlo Park buildings at Dearborn, Michigan, occurred on New Year's Eve, 1879. A crowd of 3,000 cheered wildly when the lights came on.

The Wonderful Talking Machine

None of Edison's inventions drew as much public acclaim as the phonograph, a device that one observer noted was "so simple . . . so easily understood, that one wonders why it was never before discovered."

The idea of recording sound struck Edison as he heard the speechlike tones that were made by embossed disks on his automatic telegraph repeater when it was speeded up accidentally. In 1877, he designed the first experimental model of the phonograph (right). To test it, he shouted "Mary had a little lamb" into the mouthpiece. When he heard his voice reproduced, he was astounded. "I was always afraid of things that worked the first time," he said.

Again, Edison's obstinacy nearly spoiled his achievement; he stayed with cylindrical records until 1912, when competition finally forced him to adopt more practical disk records.

A REPOSITORY OF RECORDINGS

Edison's recording studio in West Orange, New Jersey, is filled with early phonographs and records. The rolled tinfoil in the foreground is a replica of one of the first records ever made.

CANNED SOUND

The first phonograph was hand-cranked and had a grooved, foil-wrapped cylinder. Sounds passing through the mouthpiece vibrated a diaphragm, and an attached stylus pressed the vibration patterns into the foil. The sound was reproduced by a stylus and diaphragm on the other side.

The Birth of the Movies

"Good morning, Mr. Edison," said the recorded voice as the image of an assistant flickered on the screen. "Hope you like the Kinetophone." This daring attempt in 1889 at "talkies"—not successfully realized until *The Jazz Singer* in 1927—was a landmark in Edison's search for "an instrument which does for the eye what the phonograph does for the ear."

After an earlier machine *(below)* proved impractical, he developed the intermittent-motion mechanism that made moving pictures possible. Later he persuaded George Eastman to produce rolls of motion picture film, and movies were born.

At first Edison insisted that his films be viewed through his Kinetoscope, a one-viewer, peep-show affair. Only at the pleading of his distributors did he reluctantly buy the rights to a projector so that his films could be seen by a mass audience.

Edison's company made 1,700 movies, and *The Great Train Robbery* in 1903 introduced the first cowboy star, Bronco Billy Anderson. In 1961, 30 years after his death, pioneer actress Mary Pickford expressed her tribute to the stubborn wizard: "I thank you, Mr. Edison, for having been born."

THE FIRST MOVIES
Edison's first movie machine *(above)* consisted of a series of pictures spiraled around a cylinder and viewed through an eyepiece. The early film strip at right was accompanied by sound from a phonograph. The next two strips are from *The Great Train Robbery,* and at the extreme right is *The Kiss.* Superimposed are early movie equipment and a photograph of the tarpaper-covered "Black Maria," the first motion picture studio.

THEY LAUGH   THEY TALK   THEY SING

3

From Pyramid to Telegraph

A hexagonal tunnel, built by Greek engineers in the Fifth Century B.C. to house the oracle at Cumae, is based on simple mathematical principles. Ancient Greeks achieved a pleasing structural symmetry, which has been widely copied ever since.

THE ENGINEER did not get his name until the Middle Ages, when builders of battering rams, catapults and other "engines" of war were called *ingeniators* by Latin writers. By that time engineering was already thousands of years old. Along with the priesthood and soldiering, it was one of the earliest professions to emerge after men achieved civilization.

Many of the greatest works of engineering were those planned and carried out far back in the mists of antiquity. The Old Men of those bygone days had only the simplest tools and devices, and they relied largely on manpower. Nevertheless they controlled flooding rivers with dikes and transformed deserts into cropland with irrigation canals. They laid out highway and defense systems, raised temples and lofty aqueducts and crowned mountain peaks with stone cities. Some of their creations, wonders of the early world, still stand to command admiration.

By medieval times, with improved machinery harnessing water, wind and animal power, engineers could do even more. From the Middle Ages on, the pace of engineering gradually quickened until, around 1750, technology exploded into the Industrial Revolution. During the next hundred years, engineers devised steam-driven machinery, built factories, textile mills and foundries, and laced the continents with shipping canals, highways and railroads. When electricity was put to work in the latter half of the 19th Century, there seemed no limit to what engineers could accomplish. Before the century ended, they were illuminating cities, transmitting the human voice over many miles, flashing messages across the oceans via submarine cables.

From the ancient days of temple building to the laying of the first undersea telegraph lines, certain accomplishments stand out as monuments to the imagination, skill and perseverance of the engineer. Among the earliest to perform great feats of engineering were the Egyptians. By 3000 B.C. they had mastered the difficult technique of building with stone, and eventually they lined the valley of the Nile with some of the mightiest temples and tombs ever constructed. The most colossal of these is the Great Pyramid at Gizeh, completed around 2600 B.C. Even today it remains the largest cut-stone structure in the world.

The Great Pyramid was a tomb for King Khufu, or Cheops, and it was built to satisfy a basic religious belief of the Egyptians. To them, a well-preserved body was essential for enjoying life in the hereafter; therefore they attempted to safeguard the remains of their rulers with lasting tombs. From its base, 755 feet and nine inches long on each side, the Pyramid looms as high as a 40-story skyscraper. The two-and-a-quarter-million blocks of stone making up its 206 horizontal courses or layers average more than two tons apiece in weight. Some limestone blocks as heavy as 15 tons were used for its precisely fitted facing.

Every engineering problem that had to be solved in the Pyramid's construction was a problem on a monumental scale. Yet Khufu-onekh, the Old Man in charge of the project, had no wheels or horses to aid him; wheels for machinery and the domesticated horse did not appear along the Nile until 800 years later. This meant that he had no pulleys or block and tackle for hoisting and hauling, and no source of power except the muscles of massed human labor.

Orienting the gigantic structure, laying out its dimensions and leveling the foundation were problems that Khufu-onekh overcame with astonishing accuracy. He placed the Pyramid so that one side of its base follows almost exactly a true east-west line. All four sides of the base were then plotted with such precision that they come within eight inches of forming a perfect square. Each of the Pyramid's courses of stones is almost perfectly horizontal, despite the fact that Khufu-onekh had to lay out the foundation course on a rocky site that bulged upward at its center. Modern engineers think that he may have achieved a level bedding with a system of connected trenches dug around the outside of the foundation. When the trenches were filled with water its level provided a standard to fix the foundation's level. Whatever device he used, it was effective. The southeast corner of the Pyramid is only a half inch higher than the northwest corner, although the corners are 1,060 feet apart.

Next, Khufu-onekh had to erect the Pyramid itself, a job that may have taken him 20 years. Egyptologists estimate that the labor force—conscripted citizens rather than slaves—probably numbered 4,000 men at a time, with a new shift taking over every three months.

Ramps to raise the stones

Raising the enormous stones into position was a feat that would challenge today's heavy construction engineers. Most likely the job was accomplished by building a ramp of earth up to the level under construction, either on a straight slope or winding around the Pyramid on a more moderate grade. Stones for the next level, loaded on sledges, were hauled up this incline by gangs of 18 or 20 men. As the structure grew higher, so did the ramp. When the apex was completed, 481 feet above the surrounding terrain, the ramp was removed.

As formidable an engineering task as the building of the exterior was the construction of the Pyramid's inner details—the King's burial chamber and the Grand Gallery, and passages and air shafts leading to them. The roofing of these structures, particularly that of the King's chamber near the Pyramid's heart, had to withstand the tremendous weight of many higher layers of stone. To prevent the ceiling of Khufu's chamber from collapsing under this weight, the master engineer installed above it five stress-relieving compartments, one above the other and separated by 55-ton slabs of granite. During the ages, the slabs have cracked under the strain, but the roofing of the King's burial chamber remains firm.

Surpassing the Pyramid of Khufu in size but not in artistry is the Great Wall of China, the biggest work of the ancient engineers. The first Chinese emperor, Ch'in Shih Hwang Ti, began it in the Third Century B.C. to protect his empire against the Huns and their cavalry. The Wall snakes across 1,400 miles of Northern China, but because of its twistings and loops it actually measures about 2,500 miles. Hundreds of thousands of workers toiled to build its core of solidly packed earth, most of which was then faced with stone or brick masonry. Well-preserved sections of the Wall rise to an average height of 30 feet and are about 15 feet wide at the top. Along the crest of the Wall runs a paved roadway, shielded by parapets and commanded at intervals by square watchtowers.

Around the same time that the Chinese were erecting their defense line, engineering was highly developed in Rome; and over the centuries Roman engineers built many magnificent structures. Their construction technique was based largely on developments of the Greeks and others. For example, they achieved outstanding success with their widespread use of a Mesopotamian invention, the rounded arch. Composed of wedge-shaped stones or bricks locked in a curve, and braced and sustained by heavy piers, the arch distributed the weight of the overlying structure sideways as well as downward. Thus it could span openings greater than could a slab of stone resting upon two uprights. Using a succession of rounded arches, the Romans crossed rivers and valleys with bridges and aqueducts so sturdy that some still serve their original purpose.

The engineering achievements of the Middle Ages are often overlooked, yet some of them surpassed those of the Romans in boldness of conception. This was the period that saw the raising of the Gothic cathedrals, soaring monuments to the religious fervor of medieval man. With slender spires thrusting into the sky, spacious naves spanned by lofty vaults and fragile walls pierced by stained-glass windows, the cathedrals were miracles of precisely calculated balance. Depending for support upon an interplay of forces, of thrusts and counterthrusts, they represent the most daring building technique in stone ever attempted.

Each cathedral was a product of trial-and-error engineering. Because no precedents existed for structures so airy and audacious, more than one cathedral collapsed during construction and had to be rebuilt. But from failures came unique solutions to the problem of combining height and span. One solution was the pointed arch, which thrusts weight more nearly straight down upon its piers than the rounded arch. This made it possible to lift vaulted ceilings, reinforced by stone ribs, to heights of 100 feet or more. In order to span enclosures broad enough to accommodate vast congregations, another element was added—the flying buttress. The buttress, a half arch leaning against the pointed-arch pier and counteracting the outward thrust of weight on it, prevented the walls from being pushed over. The result was an enormous structure, strong yet delicate, that exalted the human spirit in an awesome setting.

Frowning walls and guarded gates

In striking contrast to the lightly built cathedrals were the massive castles of the same era, strongholds of feudal lords who frequently warred upon one another and who therefore required mighty defensive systems. Before artillery fire shattered it in World War I, the castle of Coucy, commanding the countryside near Soissons in France, was one of the most superb examples of medieval military construction. Completed in 1230 by an engineer whose name is now lost, Coucy was, like

TRANSPORTING AN OBELISK 825 feet through Rome was a major engineering feat in 1586. Crowds gathered to watch the spectacle as Domenico Fontana, the architect-engineer in charge, used more than 900 men and 74 horses to raise the 340-ton slab from its base and then lower it into a horizontal position (above). It took four months to move the obelisk to its new site in front of St. Peter's Basilica, where it stands today.

most great castles of its time, a fortress within a fortress; if a foe succeeded in penetrating its outer defenses, he still had to take a nearly impregnable inner fortification. Enclosing the court of the castle were huge parapeted walls, dominated by corner towers. The main entrance was a bridge over a ditch 65 feet wide. To cross the bridge, an enemy first had to breach its three successive gates, each guarded by watchtowers. Once across the bridge, he had to force the gate in the castle wall, a portal armed with double portcullises, or iron gratings, which could be dropped suddenly to bar the way.

Armed and provisioned against attack

If the rest of the fortress were lost, the defenders could retreat to the inner stronghold—the keep, or donjon. This mighty tower, 180 feet high and 100 feet in diameter, contained a well for water, living quarters, and storerooms for arms and provisions. Here the lord and his retainers were prepared to withstand a lengthy siege. The top level of the tower was designed for fighting off attackers in the courtyard below. An overhanging wooden platform could be quickly built around the tower's top, and holes in its flooring allowed bowmen to rain arrows down at the foe.

The castles were effective as military bulwarks until about 1500, when the increasing use of gunpowder made them obsolete. But in their day they spurred new developments in age-old engines of siege and attack —the wall-crumbling battering rams and weapons that hurled stones, darts and fireballs. Improvements in the machines of warfare brought about advances in machinery in general, particularly in mining devices.

It was in the early mines that engineers began developments in transportation and machinery that ultimately led to the Industrial Revolution and changed man's whole way of life. Railway tracks were first used underground around 1520 in the mines of Central Europe, making it easier for miners to push or pull their ore cars. The first steam engines of the late 17th and early 18th Centuries were designed to operate drainage pumps in British coal mines. More efficient pumps and improved ways to transport ore out of the mines meant that more coal and iron could be produced. This made possible increased manufacture of iron, and later of steel. These materials of great strength and lightness were cheaper and easier to use than stone for buildings and bridges, and could be easily cast into machinery parts. Their large-scale production was an advance as vital to technology as the introduction of steam and electric power.

In 1700 iron was too expensive for anything except cannon; by 1815 it was so economical that it was replacing wooden plumbing pipes in homes. The big change began in 1709, when Abraham Darby, an English ironmaster, found that coal converted into coke could be used instead of charcoal to smelt iron on a commercial scale.

With iron readily available, especially wrought iron, engineers were able to cross wide bodies of water with suspension bridges, weblike structures whose delicate appearance belied their soundness. Such bridg-

ARCH

STRUT

BUTTRESS

THE FLYING BUTTRESS was developed by medieval engineers to prevent the lofty arches of Gothic cathedrals from buckling outward. It carried the roof's lateral thrust (1) through a strut *(dashed line)* to a heavy standing buttress, whose own weight exerted a strong downward force (2). The net effect of these lateral and downward forces (1 and 2) was a stabilizing force (3) directed toward the bottom of the buttress. More than one cathedral collapsed because medieval engineers built the buttresses by trial and error. They lacked the knowledge of the laws of force, now part of every engineer's training.

es supported their roadways on chains or cables strong enough to eliminate many of the piers needed for stone or wooden bridges. Also, suspension spans could be raised so high that they would not interfere with ships passing beneath. The idea of hanging a bridge in air was not new; the Incas of South America and other ancient peoples had used suspension bridges to conquer chasms. But their bridges had been only slender, swaying footpaths, held up by cables of braided fiber or leather.

The prototype of all great modern suspension bridges was the one Thomas Telford built across the Menai Strait, separating the mainland of Wales from the Welsh island of Anglesey. Telford, a famous Old Man of British engineering, began his bridge in 1818 as a link in another of his masterworks—the 300-mile highway he built to speed travel between London and the Anglesey port of Holyhead on the Irish Sea. Telford planned a central span of 579 feet, suspended 102 feet above the water. Supporting the bridge's two parallel roadways were 16 chains made up of flat, wrought iron segments, or eyebars, each about 10 feet long. From their anchorages on either shore, the chains extended across the strait and were held aloft by two stone towers, one near the mainland at the town of Caernarvon and the other off the island of Anglesey.

Inspiration in a fifers' tune

The raising of the first suspension chain of the center span was an exciting moment. Telford had the chain spread on a long, narrow raft and floated the raft into position between the towers. One end of the chain was then secured to the top of the mainland tower; the other end was attached to ropes passing over the tower at Anglesey. While a band of Welsh fifers played a merry tune, 150 workmen turned a giant hoisting capstan behind the Anglesey tower, hauling that end of the chain up from the water. Telford later wrote: "In one hour and thirty-five minutes after they commenced hoisting, the chain was raised to its proper curvature and fastened. . . . I then ascended, and satisfied myself that by this juncture had been formed a continuous and safe chain from the Caernarvon fastening in the rock to that in Anglesey. Having announced this fact, a loud and general shout of exhultation arose from the workmen and the numerous spectators who had assembled to witness this novel operation." Two of the workmen became so exuberant on the ale that was generously poured that they crawled from one tower to the other on the newly strung chain. When the bridge was completed in 1826, its overall length of 1,710 feet made it the longest suspension span of its time. Largely rebuilt in 1939, it is still in use today.

Toward the end of the steam-powered Industrial Revolution, when electricity's energy was harnessed, engineers encountered a brand-new field to challenge their ingenuity. Now engineering monuments began to take a different form. Some were invisible, relaying messages through the atmosphere or across the ocean floor. Yet they were just as impressive as the great structural achievements of earlier days.

By 1837, William Cooke and Charles Wheatstone in Britain and Sam-

A REVERSIBLE WATERWHEEL, designed to lift water out of mine shafts, was one of dozens of ingenious machines which 16th Century engineers used for mining. To turn the wheel, an operator (O) pulled levers to direct water from a reservoir (A) into one of the two rows of scoops, set into the rim of the wheel so that they faced in opposite directions. By channeling water into the left row (G), he made the wheel turn a drum (K) that lowered a leather bucket into the mine. He reversed the direction of the wheel to raise the filled bucket by directing the stream of water to the other row (H).

uel F. B. Morse in the United States had independently developed the telegraph, the first practical application of electricity. This paved the way for another triumph of electrical engineering—the laying of the first transatlantic telegraph cable. In its day, the event stirred up almost as much excitement as did the first space flights in our time.

Several submarine cables were operating successfully in the English Channel and the Mediterranean by 1855. Thus engineers had every reason to believe that a similar line of communication could be laid across the Atlantic, linking Ireland and Newfoundland. In 1856, Cyrus W. Field, an adventurous American business promoter, joined with British interests to form a company supporting the project.

A 2,000-mile undertaking

The problems posed by cable-laying on such a vast scale were staggering. In the first place, the distance between Ireland and Newfoundland was far greater than had ever been spanned by cable before—nearly 2,000 miles. Before a foot of cable could be reeled out, sounding apparatus had to be devised to determine the character of the ocean's bottom along the proposed route. Too jagged a bottom might cut the cable; undersea chasms would cause it to sag and possibly break. Next came the task of making the cable itself—2,500 miles of it, designed for maximum strength and flexibility and coated with special insulation to protect it from erosion by seawater. The completed cable, too bulky a load for a single ship, had to be divided between two vessels.

In their first attempts to lay the cable the engineers encountered repeated difficulties but they refused to be daunted. In 1857 and again in 1858, the cable was laid partway, only to break and disappear into the ocean's depths. In August of 1858 completion of the full span was celebrated with a wild torchlight parade in New York City and an exchange of appropriate messages between Queen Victoria and President Buchanan—but after four weeks and 400 cablegrams, the cable went dead, its insulation eaten away by oxidation and torn by rocks.

The Civil War in America halted further cable-laying attempts until 1865, but meanwhile developments were underway that ultimately led to success. One improvement was a stronger cable, with tougher insulation. The core of the new cable, seven strands of copper wire protected by four layers of gutta-percha, was covered by tarred hemp and further protected by a spiral wrapping of 10 steel wires, each wire wound with hemp saturated with oxidation-resistant preservative. Another innovation of supreme importance was a contribution of science—the mirror galvanometer developed by the eminent Scottish physicist, Sir William Thomson (Lord Kelvin). This instrument consisted of a small magnet and mirror enclosed in a wire coil and suspended by a filament of silk.

TELEGRAPHIC LINKS between two worlds, the early transatlantic cables stretched nearly 2,000 nautical miles between Newfoundland and Ireland. The first cable was considered an engineering marvel when it was laid down in 1858 and carried the first official message to Ireland: "Glory to God in the highest, on earth peace, good will to men." But the cable failed after transmitting only 400 messages and it was not until 1866 that a second cable (bottom line) was successfully installed.

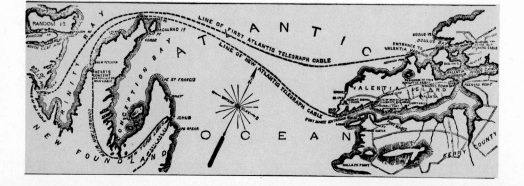

From this assembly conducting wires led to the cable as it was being paid out. So sensitive was the galvanometer that the slightest change in the flow of current through the cable caused the magnet to move, and the mirror attached to it reflected a spot of light onto a graduated scale. An almost imperceptible motion of the magnet produced a large movement of the light upon the scale, indicating that the cable had been damaged. Thus the cable could be quickly retrieved and the damage corrected.

For the 1865 attempt, it had been decided to spin the cable out from a single ship. At that time there was only one ship in the world big enough to carry the enormous burden—3,000 miles of cable weighing 5,000 tons. That vessel was the *Great Eastern*, an iron monster 693 feet long and driven by sail as well as by steam engines which turned both paddle wheels and a screw propeller. An audacious achievement of marine engineering, the *Great Eastern* had been a financial failure as a luxury liner. When Cyrus Field engaged her for cable-laying she was a great white elephant of a ship, too big for the docking facilities of the day and outrageously expensive to operate. But lay the cable she did.

In July 1865, the *Great Eastern* steamed away from Ireland, spinning cable in her wake. After 1,200 miles, a defective length of cable slipped through the paying-out machinery; as it was being reeled in, the cable suddenly snapped. William Howard Russell, a London *Times* correspondent who reported the voyage, echoed the dismay aboard ship when he wrote: "The cable parted . . . and flashed into the sea. The cable gone! gone forever down in that fearful depth! There around us lay the placid Atlantic . . . and not a dimple to show where lay so many hopes buried." After 10 days' grappling for the cable in water two and a half miles deep, the spot was marked with a buoy and the search abandoned.

Lasting links beneath the sea

Cyrus Field's original cable company failed, but a new one was organized for still another attempt in the summer of 1866. Dogged persistence finally paid off—this time the *Great Eastern* carried a new cable all the way to Newfoundland. Appropriately, it was brought ashore at a point called Heart's Content. A few weeks later the giant steamer returned to the buoy in mid-Atlantic and fished up the cable lost the year before. Its end was spliced to another coil of cable to form a second submarine communication link between Europe and North America.

Laying the Atlantic cable was not the work of any one Old Man. It called for precise teamwork by marine, electrical and mechanical engineers, physicists, oceanographers and many other specialists. Thus it may be said to have marked the beginning of the modern era of great engineering accomplishments, when experts in many fields pool their knowledge and skills to achieve a common goal.

LAYING THE ATLANTIC CABLE in 1858 was a task requiring a pair of ships with specially designed holds. On the four decks of the *Niagara*, shown in cross section above, the 1,500-ton weight was distributed evenly, preventing damage to the coiled cable and to the ship. The cable was wound around four wooden cones and guided onto the deck by means of suspended wire hoops *(below)*, which kept it from kinking as it passed into the sea.

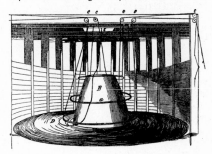

Durable Works
of Ancient Engineers

In a very real sense, civilization itself depends on the engineer; for civilization begins when people gather in cities, and cities cannot exist without engineers. Long before 2000 B.C., when Hammurabi was king in fabled Babylon, ancient engineers had confronted and had found basic solutions for the same sort of urban problems that continue to challenge engineers today: water supply, communications, defense, the design of large structures.

The record of ancient engineers' achievements is preserved in the surviving remnants of their work scattered throughout the world, from the ancient waterwheels and aqueducts of Syria *(opposite)* to the mountain fortresses of the Incas in Peru. The engineers who built these structures used only rudimentary tools, often substituted ingenuity and intuition for detailed plans and even created their own on-the-job technology. But they succeeded in solving many of the practical problems of their times, and in doing so these early engineers left a far greater legacy than their creations in wood, brick and stone: they established the tradition and skills that form the basis of civilization to this day.

WHEELS TO LIFT WATER
Ancient waterwheels called norias, similar to those that had appeared in the Near East by 350 B.C., were in use until recently in Syria to irrigate farmland and to supply water to the city of Hamāh. The wheels shown here were mentioned in Roman writings of 15 B.C.; they turned with the current and carried water to raised aqueducts *(right)* in hollowed-out sections of the outer rim.

Man-made Mountains

The Sumerians—like many ancient civilizations—felt that gods should be worshiped from high places. But Sumer's cities lay on the flat plain of Mesopotamia, so towers had to be built for the temples. The problem was compounded by the lack of strong materials, such as wood and stone.

Undismayed, Sumerian engineers used what was available—clay bricks or earth—to build the temple towers called ziggurats. The one shown here consisted of rectangles of sun-dried brick. Because such masses of brick tended to crumble under their own weight, the ziggurat was erected in stepped layers up to 50 feet high, each layer held in place by thick walls

of stronger, kiln-fired bricks. The solid structure resembled a many-tiered wedding cake, with ramps running up to the top, where there may have been a crowning temple. Later Near Eastern civilizations also built ziggurats: both the Hanging Gardens of Babylon and the Biblical Tower of Babel may have been such structures.

AN IMPOSING RELIC
The ziggurat of Ur, dedicated to the moon god Nanna, was built around 2100 B.C. Its base covers 30,000 square feet and the surviving walls are eight feet thick. It may once have been 70 feet high—an imposing size by Sumerian standards—with exotic gardens gracing its terraces. Even after 20 centuries of neglect, it testifies to the daring and skill of its builders.

The Arteries
of an Empire

Roman engineers, perfecting techniques used by the Etruscans, Greeks and Carthaginians, produced a network of superb roads like the Appian Way (right), parts of which carried traffic for more than 22 centuries. In the early days of the Roman Republic, all roads indeed led to—and from —Rome. Radiating from the city were four types, classified by width from the one-foot *semita*, or footpath, to the eight-foot *via*, or highway. But as Rome's Empire grew, so did the length and breadth of its roads. By 200 A.D. more than 50,000 miles of roads carried Roman civilization as far as England and Asia Minor (below).

The roads were as straight as topography permitted. When necessary, Roman engineers built bridges, embankments, cuts and tunnels to make routes more direct. Layers of convenient material, like earth, stone and crushed rock, formed a roadbed. The surface of stone slabs, cobblestones or gravel was sloped for drainage. The Romans made their roadbeds very deep—up to eight feet, as compared to around two feet for present roads. For the builders apparently meant them to last as long as the Empire—in other words, forever.

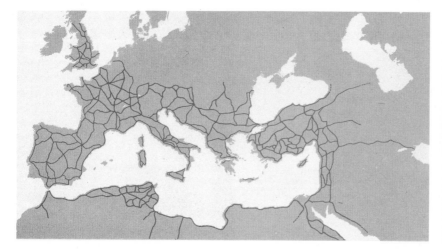

AN INTRICATE WEB OF HIGHWAYS
In the Second Century A.D. Roman highways *(above)* embraced most of Europe and circled the Mediterranean. Many were built as military roads, enabling the legions to move overland quickly. Later they became the principal routes of transportation and commerce that kept Roman civilization alive after Rome fell into ruin.

THE "QUEEN OF LONG ROADS"
The Appian Way, begun in 312 B.C., was the first and most famous of Roman *vias*. It carried Roman legions to Brindisi, for embarkation to Greece and Asia Minor. As Rome's main highway to the south, it was improved over the centuries. This tomb-lined portion is 12 feet wide —a three-lane highway by Roman standards.

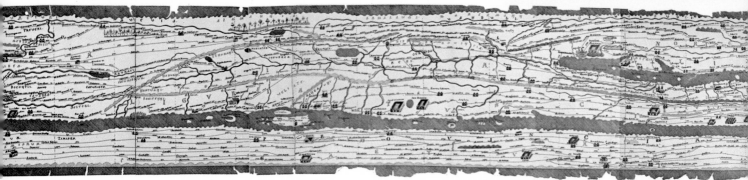

This copy of a Roman road map of 350 A.D. traces the routes of the major highways of that period. So that all the roads could be included

on a long scroll, geographical features are deliberately distorted: the bottom strip is North Africa; the horizontal peninsula above it is Italy.

Water for a Thirsty City

An essential to any civilization is an adequate water supply, and as early as 312 B.C. Roman engineers began to build a water system on a scale that had never before been attempted. By 226 A.D., 11 aqueducts were delivering 260 million gallons of fresh water each day, making possible elaborate public baths as well as numerous fountains brimming with free water for Rome's million inhabitants.

From sources in the hills as distant as 30 miles, water was carried by gravity flow through channels and conduits to a point above the Roman plain. There it was transferred to the arched stone bridges which provided a uniform gradient into the city. Pressure from these elevated aqueducts propelled the water through an elaborate network of lead and clay pipes that ran beneath the city's streets.

A PIGGYBACK AQUEDUCT
One aqueduct atop another can be seen in this impressive structure near Rome. Practical Roman engineers used elevated portions of the older Claudian aqueduct, completed in 52 A.D., to carry the Anio Novus system. The two rectangular channels, the lower of which is clearly visible, delivered over 50 million gallons of water a day into Rome from mountain springs.

ARCH UPON ARCH
The well-preserved Pont du Gard, with its perfect form and three rows of arches, is a triumph of Roman engineering. Built in 19 B.C. as part of the water supply system for the garrison in Nimes, France (the Roman Nemausus), it carried an aqueduct 150 feet above the Gard River.

The Lost City of the Incas

High on a mountain ridge in Peru lies Machu Picchu, the lost city of the ancient Incas. A self-sufficient and virtually impregnable fortress, it may have been the final sanctuary of the Inca priests and sacred Virgins of the Sun after the conquest of Peru by Spanish conquistadors in the 16th Century. Machu Picchu ("Old Peak") is an awesome example of Incan skill in stonemasonry and in engineering.

The city was built of granite, mostly quarried from surrounding bedrock, and was protected on two sides by 2,000-foot gorges and on a third side by the steep rise of an adjoining peak. The only approach was a narrow, fortified trail leading from the Urubamba River. Small wonder that unconquered Machu Picchu, a ghost town after its last few inhabitants died, was not rediscovered until 1911.

DUAL-PURPOSE TERRACES

The terraces of Machu Picchu, carved into its lower slopes, may have been designed to serve two purposes. Covered with earth and planted with corn, potatoes, tomatoes and beans, they gave the city its own food source. But the terraces also formed an inner defense against possible attackers, who would have had to mount a mammoth staircase of 10-foot steps.

A MOUNTAIN METROPOLIS

Machu Picchu was engineered as a compact city complete with its own food and water supply system. Still visible are its tiered rows of houses and garden terraces, surrounding a spacious central plaza. The highest structure is a raised altar that was dedicated to Inti, the sacred sun.

SIGNS OF A STONEMASON'S SKILL

A block of granite, discarded by the stonemasons of Machu Picchu, shows how the city's basic building material was reduced to size. Wedges of wood were inserted into small holes chipped into the rock. When soaked with water, the wedges expanded and split the block.

An Age of Cathedrals

The soaring symbols of Christianity in the Middle Ages were the splendid cathedrals that rose in many European cities. Medieval engineers tried various structural forms in their zeal to build cathedrals higher and more spacious than the tried and proven round Roman arches would support. Sometimes they failed and their half-built cathedrals collapsed. But finally they succeeded in combining the features of the pointed arch, groined vault and flying buttress to produce their Gothic cathedrals—magnificent living monuments in stone and glass.

THE CATHEDRAL BUILDERS
Building a cathedral was often a task that occupied hundreds of craftsmen for decades. In this exaggerated version of the building of an imaginary cathedral, drawn by a medieval artist, the master builder, or supervising engineer, receives a royal visitor in his pulpitlike post.

A VIEW OF A VAULT

The Cathedral of St. Etienne in Bourges, France, completed in the 13th Century and partially rebuilt in the 16th Century, boasts a groined vault more than 120 feet high. The ribs brace the vault and help distribute its weight among the columns inside and the buttresses outside.

VISIBLE MEANS OF SUPPORT

Flying buttresses—masonry props—were the answer of medieval engineers to the problem of supporting a vault without thick walls. At St. Etienne *(above)* the firmly anchored buttresses supported the powerful outward push of the vault, permitting thin, windowed walls.

A Monument in a Mine Shaft

The very word "engineer" refers to engines, and simple machinery—like the waterwheel—was used by virtually every ancient civilization. But it was not until the Middle Ages that engineers began to think in terms of laborsaving machinery that would increase productivity.

By the 15th Century, human muscles had been generally replaced by water, wind and animal power, often harnessed to huge wooden machines like the one shown here. This horse-driven hoist was used to lift heavy loads of salt from a Polish mine. An improved version of an ancient machine, it was used as late as the 18th Century. By then, in the coal mines of England, a new breed of engineers were applying new mechanical principles and steam power to cast-iron machines. Their development of the steam engine—originally employed to pump water from the mines—laid the groundwork for the Industrial Revolution and made animal-powered machines obsolete. Today this wooden hoist, restored and in perfect working order, is maintained strictly as an underground tourist attraction.

AN EIGHT-HORSEPOWER ENGINE
This reconstructed hoist in a salt mine at Wieliczka, Poland, is little changed from its medieval prototype. Eight paired horses were used to turn the vertical reel whose ropes raised or lowered salt and heavy equipment by means of two pulleys fixed over a nearby shaft. Earlier hoists at Wieliczka, where salt has been mined since the 11th Century, were turned by hand.

4

The Modern Method: Systems Engineering

Testing the instruments of a moon-landing craft, an engineer simulates a space docking with the televised image of a parent vehicle.

THE OLD MEN OF ENGINEERING, who knew every detail of a job and bossed each step in its development, had achieved wonders in their time through the use of trial-and-error methods and the data in handbooks. Yet their projects, great as they were, seem child's play beside some of those undertaken by today's science-oriented engineers.

As the development of new techniques led engineers to the production of electronically controlled communication apparatus, computers, radar, nuclear weapons, missiles, supersonic airplanes and spacecraft, the work became so complex that it was no longer possible for any one person to understand all the parts in a single device. The one-man approach of the Old Men had to be replaced by the highly sophisticated arrangement called systems engineering. Today specialists in many fields work on separate parts of a problem under the direction of program managers. These managers may not know the details of each specialist's work but they know enough about their project's overall design, the interrelationship of its various parts and its functional requirements to guide and coordinate the completion of the task—hopefully on schedule and within the budget.

Systems engineering involves the planning and dividing of work to achieve orderly completion of such vastly complicated projects as the Ballistic Missile Early Warning System radar screen in the far North, the Tennessee Valley and St. Lawrence hydroelectric power systems and the Apollo lunar landing missions. The basic idea underlying systems engineering is simple: it is the organization of a multitude of separate functions into an integrated whole that will achieve one desired main objective. An elementary example of a working system is a moving automobile, in which the judgment and reflexes of the driver are combined with the car's fuel, ignition, transmission, steering gear, brakes and throttle to produce one desired output: controlled and orderly travel. Far more complex are the systems of large airplanes or of computers, with their thousands of components, intricately linked.

What is not so simple about systems engineering is the word "systems" itself. It is often used to mean several different things. There can be all sorts of systems within one large system; moreover, several large systems can be joined to form a still larger system. A spacecraft, which is called a system, consists of the following full-fledged systems: a fuel system, a propulsion system, a navigation and guidance system, a communications system, a stabilization system, a reaction control system and an instrumentation system. In addition, the spacecraft's flight is directed from the ground by a flight control system. And each of these systems has one or more subsystems. The difference between systems and subsystems is that, generally speaking, a system is concerned with functional requirements while a subsystem provides the machinery that meets the requirements. Along with technical demands, the planning and creation of a large system has to meet such standards as safety, health, reliability, budget, time and, in many cases, legality and esthetic taste.

The greatest engineering system ever attempted, dwarfing in size and scope the most spectacular undertakings of the past, is the Apollo Program, whose bold objective upon its inception in 1960 was the landing of astronauts on the moon and their safe return to earth. By the time the first landing team, astronauts Neil Armstrong and Edwin "Buzz" Aldrin, touched down on July 20, 1969, the program had cost the United States an estimated $24 billion. At the peak of planning and development in 1966, it involved the coordinated efforts of nearly 20,000 industrial companies, universities and research centers and some 350,000 engineers, scientists and technicians.

Within the overall framework of this gigantic project, engineers set up many component systems and subsystems that were tremendous engineering enterprises in themselves. Perhaps the most celebrated of these involved the construction of 15 spidery-legged Lunar Modules, one of which, Number 7 on the assembly line, became a "lifeboat" for the crew of Apollo 13 in April 1970, when their moon-bound spaceship was damaged by an explosion some 200,000 miles from earth. The LMs, as the 16- to 18-ton modules are called, were designed by Grumman Aerospace Corporation to transport and shelter two of each mission's three astronauts on their relatively brief excursions from the orbiting spacecraft to the moon and back. That one of them in an emergency could sustain three men in space for three and a half days was a surprising and fortunate development. The Apollo engineers, however, had taken into account such possible emergencies and had designed the systems of the LM and the other two units of the spacecraft, the Command and Service Modules, so that they could be used in more than one way.

Functioning in space

The compound vehicle starts its journey from the earth with an immense thrust from a mammoth three-stage Saturn V rocket, which is as tall as a 36-story building. During the 238,000-mile, 72-hour trip, the astronauts coast along in the Command Module while the Service Module, strapped and bolted to the astronauts' habitat, delivers electrical power, oxygen and water through a giant umbilical cord. The Service Module also houses the spacecraft's most powerful rocket engine. The craft's third unit, the LM, is carried into space in the top section of the Saturn V booster rocket. In space, the Command and Service Modules separate from the booster rocket and do an about-face maneuver to dock nose-to-nose with the LM. The now useless booster rocket is jettisoned.

Sixty miles or so above the moon the spacecraft swings into a lunar orbit, and the astronauts squeeze through hatches into the LM. If all systems check out, the astronaut remaining in the Command Module seals the hatches; and, like a dinghy lowered from a mother ship, the LM descends to the moon's surface. One engine gets the astronauts down; another lifts them off in their cabin, leaving the landing section of the LM behind. Once they have returned to the parent craft, the LM's ascent stage is sent to crash on the lunar surface.

Grumman's planning for the construction of the LM was a graphic example of the way engineers approach and manage a large-scale system of enormous complexity. In November 1962 Grumman, in competition with other major aeronautical engineering firms, won the National Aeronautics and Space Administration's prime contract for the lunar vehicle. But long before the award was announced, Grumman engineers and NASA scientists had been studying such a scheme. An interoffice memo in the company's files at Bethpage, New York, written in 1958 when few people were thinking about these things, outlines a discussion at Grumman about the possibility of a manned trip to the moon in a vehicle like the LM that would ferry astronauts between an orbiting parent spacecraft and the moon's surface.

During the next few years, a group at Grumman spent thousands of man-hours working out the details of such a vehicle. As a result, in 1961, when President Kennedy was pressing for faster action in the race for the moon, Grumman was ready to submit to the government space agency an exhaustive "Lunar Module Study."

Advance planning pays off

"That study was a book about four inches thick, filled with data on requirements," recalls Saul Ferdman, Grumman's Director of Advanced Space Programs. "People think an engineering company like this one doesn't do much real work on a project until after it lands the contract. We spent about four million dollars, and built a new space engineering plant here at Bethpage for the LM work, before we even received a request for a bid. When we submitted our proposal, it not only had complete technical studies and designs of the system—it also had a complete management organization, with the names and biographies of all the key men who would work on the LM program. In other words, the talent was hired, assigned and ready to start work. The proposal also listed all the subcontractors and told why each one had been selected.

"Then NASA asked us and other leading companies to answer twenty technical questions, designed to find out how much we really knew about the whole problem, and they stipulated that the twenty questions had to be answered in eighty typewritten pages—no more. Some of the proposals NASA had received from bidders on the Apollo Program the year before had been as long as a five-foot bookshelf and they wanted no more of *that*. All this, mind you, before we had any idea of whether or not we were going to win the contract award. Our answers to the twenty questions received the highest rating. After a thorough review and plant inspection by NASA, we got word that the LM contract was ours."

Grumman then set up the LM management program, which operates as an independent company within the Grumman corporation. In addition to its technical divisions, the LM program has its own business department with managers of purchasing, cost controls, contract administration and subcontracting; there are also departments of quality control, administrative services and manufacturing—a far cry from the days when an Old Man bossing a large engineering job could carry all of

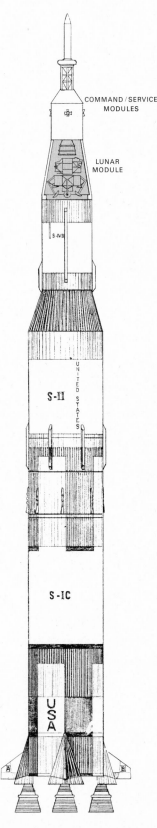

SATURN V, the 363-foot rocket built to send three astronauts into orbit around the moon, consists of three separate stages (labeled S-IC, S-II and S-IVB) with a total of 11 engines. They lift a 100,000-pound payload that includes, neatly folded inside the nose, the LM (Lunar Module). This vehicle later separates from the Command/Service Modules and carries two of the astronauts to a landing on the moon.

his accounts and business papers for the project tucked away in his hat.

The 52 managers and principal engineers named in Grumman's first proposal represented only a small fraction of the talent that has since been employed on the project. In early 1968, more than 7,200 engineers and technicians were working on the LM in Grumman's plant at Bethpage. In addition, many key engineers at NASA's Manned Spacecraft Center at Houston, Texas, contributed to the LM's development. Each engineer in charge of a system or subsystem at Grumman had an opposite number at the space agency's Houston center with whom he met regularly to discuss his progress and problems. Although Grumman was the prime contractor, it handled less than half of the total work—many more thousands of engineers and technicians were involved in the moon vehicle at the plants of various subcontractors around the country. For example, the LM's descent engine was built by TRW Inc. at Redondo Beach, California; the ascent engine was constructed by North American Rockwell's Rocketdyne Division at Canoga Park, California. Maintaining such an array of engineering and technical skill demanded a vast amount of money: by 1970 the project had cost some $1.6 billion.

The systems managers

Grumman went into actual operation on construction of the moon vehicle in January 1963. The burden of organizing and running the project was handed to Joseph G. Gavin Jr., now a Senior Vice President of Grumman. Gavin was the obvious choice to head the job since he had been directing technical work at Bethpage for the previous five years, including the original LM studies and Grumman's Orbiting Astronomical Observatory, a 4,500-pound precision scientific satellite. A graduate of the Massachusetts Institute of Technology with honors in aeronautical engineering, Gavin had already had 20 years of experience in spacecraft, missile and jet aircraft designing. His top assistant was Robert S. Mullaney, LM Program Manager, an aeronautical engineer who studied industrial management as a Sloan Fellow at M.I.T. The Engineering Manager, William Rathke, had had conspicuous success as a project engineer and program manager for naval aircraft. Thomas J. Kelly was LM Project Manager. Young and energetic, Kelly had done outstanding work as a systems engineer and had played an important role in developing the LM concept.

The first thing the managers had to do was to study the main requirements for landing such a vehicle on the moon and getting it safely back into space after its exploration mission, requirements that had already been outlined in the preliminary proposal. Then they had to parcel out these problems to separate systems managers charged with responsibility for solving these puzzling questions. Gavin and Mullaney planned

THE SCHEME FOR LANDING on the surface of the moon *(below)* is typical of the Apollo project's intricate engineering. The Command/Service Modules, or CSM, coupled with the LM, brakes (1) and turns in its orbit (2). Two astronauts crawl into the LM, which separates and orients itself (3) as it descends, braking (4) so that it lands at less than one and a half miles per hour (5). The CSM stays in orbit (6) until the LM returns.

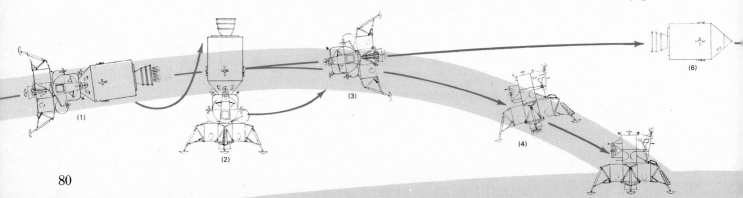

nine major systems concerned with the LM's functional needs. One system, for example, was human factors, the matching of equipment to the men who would use it. Instruments would have to be designed and arranged for quick, accurate comprehension; controls would have to be set up for sure, easy operation; windows would have to be arranged to provide the clear views necessary for accurate maneuvering. Another system was devoted entirely to thorough and extensive advance testing of the LM's reliability. Still other systems concentrated on the structure of the vehicle, its flight characteristics and control, and temperature conditions inside and outside. Finally, there was an integration system to make sure that all the complex parts fitted into a workable whole.

Within these nine systems, 10 major subsystems were set up to develop the physical equipment—the hardware—that would enable the moon vehicle to accomplish its purpose. The LM's overall structure was a subsystem, its descent and ascent engines were separate subsystems, and its guidance and control were a subsystem. Other subsystem managers concerned themselves with the power supply source, the communication links to the parent spacecraft and earth, and the monitoring devices for keeping tabs on the LM's intricate parts during flight. Explosive disconnectors, such as those that separate the vehicle's two stages when the upper section blasts off from the moon to return to the parent vehicle, were still another subsystem; so were cabin environment—oxygen supply, pressure and temperature—and crew provisions, including instrument panels, space suits and the life-support packs the men would wear when they ventured out into the hostile lunar environment.

Saving precious pounds

Two problems were especially troublesome in designing the LM: weight and reliability. Because each extra pound of equipment requires many extra pounds of fuel to lift it into space, the engineers were under constant pressure to eliminate every ounce that could be spared. For instance, the astronauts' need for a television camera in addition to a still camera was a matter of considerable debate; getting rid of one camera would save a precious five pounds. Also, the engineers literally shaved unnecessary ounces of metal from the vehicle itself. "Eliminating nonessential equipment saves weight, and so does shaving away metal in a manner that does not endanger reliability," said John Coutinho, who supervised work on the reliability system. "And reliability on this project was all-important because we had no margin of error. Everything *had* to work exactly right the first time."

To ensure the reliability of the LM and the success of its missions, a fantastic array of testing devices was set up at various space centers across the nation. Among these devices were huge steel chambers at

TO BLAST OFF FROM THE MOON, the LM uses its lower portion as a launching pad, leaving it behind (7) while ascending into lunar orbit, again near the CSM (8). The LM maneuvers to bring its hatch opposite that of the CSM, permitting the astronauts to crawl back into the CSM (9). The LM, its job completed, is jettisoned (10) and the astronauts fire their engine to get out of the lunar orbit and begin the return to earth.

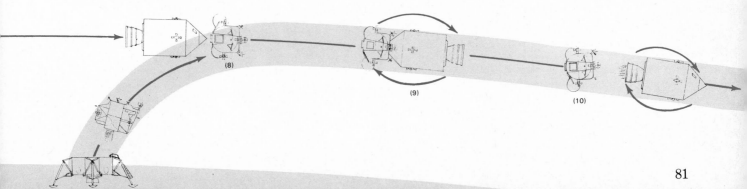

White Sands, New Mexico, in which the vehicle's descent and ascent engines were fired under conditions duplicating those to be found on the moon. At NASA's research center at Langley Field, Virginia, a gigantic structure of steel girders, more than 250 feet high and 400 feet long, permitted still another group of engineers to simulate the LM's landing on the moon. Suspended from a crane rolling along the upper length of this framework was a full-scale research model resembling the LM. As the model moved back and forth and up and down, it pitched, rolled and yawed, allowing engineers and astronauts to perfect the maneuvers needed to set the LM down on the lunar surface.

A Texas moonscape

Even more remarkable was the moonscape that was built for testing purposes at Houston, Texas, by the NASA engineers. This replica of the moon's surface was strewn with rubble and pumice, tons of slag and great chunks of lava rock, and contained several large craters 15 feet deep. This desolate, man-made lunar surface was useful for perfecting the design of the scientific tools and equipment used by the astronauts and also for making time-and-motion studies of the LMs' crews in their space suits. A full-scale model of the lunar vehicle in the midst of the moonscape gave astronauts practice in getting in and out of the LM.

The rigor and exhaustiveness of this advance testing, involving so many groups of engineering specialists in so many places, would flabbergast a typical Old Man, who in his day could build a new machine, try it out, and if it didn't work, go back to the drafting board to design a different one. "Old-fashioned trial-and-error methods have no place in today's large systems engineering," emphasized Reliability Director Coutinho. "In a system like the LM, costing over a billion dollars and several years of time, a component part might be changed or revised, but the overall system could not afford to be completely altered for a second try once it had been committed to production."

There have been many basic changes in the LM system since Grumman started to work on it in 1963, and there have been myriad changes in operational planning and in the LM's design details. For example, it was first assumed that radio signals from a control station on earth would take so long to travel to the moon, 238,000 miles away, that they could not be of much use in guiding the astronauts in the LM. The engineers of the communications subsystem discovered, however, that the time lag—one and a quarter seconds—in receipt of information sent from the ground would not handicap operations. Consequently, data and instructions transmitted from earth came to play a larger role in the mission than originally planned. "We found that we could keep in close touch with the astronauts all during the mission," said an LM engineer. "Each operation could be timed to almost the exact second. And we could do that best using both our computers on the ground and in the LM."

Computer calculations signaled from the earth play an especially crucial role in bringing the LM up from the moon to the rendezvous with the

Command Module, orbiting about 60 miles out in lunar space. In order for the two space vehicles to meet, the timing of the ascent and the LM's propulsion speed must be carefully coordinated with the position and speed of the parent craft. If the LM's blastoff from the moon's surface should be delayed more than five minutes after the scheduled time, the astronauts would either have to wait two hours for the parent craft to make another orbit around the moon or take off and go into their own orbit until a rendezvous could be worked out.

"If it weren't for our computers and the mathematicians who know how to get answers from computers, the two ships wouldn't meet at all," another of LM's engineers pointed out. "For that matter, if it weren't for the computers we couldn't even have considered a trip to the moon. No human being could calculate the trajectories and the propulsion and the fuel requirements accurately enough to make such a complex rendezvous mission work out successfully."

The decision to rely more on ground-based computers was a change in procedure, not in the design of the LM vehicle. But one major component was modified after its original conception: the landing gear. The success or failure of the landing on the moon, as well as the lives of the astronauts themselves, depended largely upon this structure. To prevent damage to the LM, it was essential that it touch down on the lunar surface in a more or less upright position. If the landing gear failed to accomplish this, and the lunar vehicle toppled over on its side, the results would be disastrous.

Unpredictable hazards of a lunar landing

This problem was thrown at the engineers of the landing-gear subsystem, who had to allow for dangers they could not predict with any certainty. For one thing, the character of the lunar terrain was a mystery; the engineers had to consider that it might be firm in some places, a thin and fragile crust in others, and in still other places it might consist of fine dust many feet deep. Complicating this potential hazard was the moon's weak gravitation, only one sixth as strong as the earth's, which would lessen the LM's stability during its descent. Another factor that had to be taken into account was the velocity with which the LM would approach the moon.

"We ran hundreds of computer tests to determine the landing velocity," explained William Rathke, the LM's Engineering Manager, "and happily we found that it wouldn't be as fast as we first figured it would be. Then we did intensive testing to see how the landing gear would stand up under various conditions, such as a skidding, slanted landing, or a landing on a slope."

As first conceived, the landing gear consisted of five legs. But testing demonstrated that four slender legs attached to outriggers would provide all the stability needed to settle the LM into an upright position even if it landed on a moderate slope. Besides, a gear with only four legs instead of five would save weight.

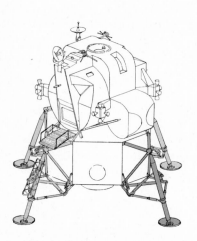

THE LM'S FOUR LEGS *(above)*, pushed out into a landing position by small explosive charges, were designed to meet a wide range of eventualities. To absorb shocks, the telescoping steel legs were filled with aluminum honeycomb *(below)* that compresses under impact *(below, right)* to a fraction of its original size. In addition, broad pads were attached to the legs to help support the LM on loose or uneven lunar terrain.

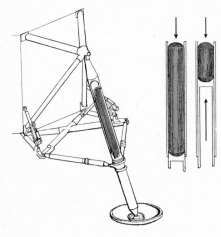

Not only did the landing gear have to set the LM down in a stable, upright position; it also had to protect the LM from damage by absorbing most of the impact shock. The subsystem engineers solved this problem by filling the legs and their supporting struts with a crushable aluminum material that looks like a bee's honeycomb; on impact the legs would contract somewhat, compressing the honeycomb. Furthermore, the landing gear had to be protected from the heat of the descent engine's exhaust, which would bounce back from the moon's surface as the LM made its touchdown. The heat problem was solved, over a period of time, by wrapping layers and layers of aluminized Mylar, a polyester film, around the LM's legs. Only six weeks before the historic launch of Apollo 11, Grumman engineers designed and tested further thermal protection after NASA decided to keep the descent engine burning to the moment of lunar contact, instead of shutting it off a few seconds earlier as originally planned. Dramatically, the first moon-landing LM, the Eagle, was already in its cocoonlike casing atop the Saturn V at Kennedy Space Center when workers applied up to 50 more layers of Mylar.

Of the hundreds of complex problems that had to be solved in designing the LM, one seemingly simple detail plagued the human-factors engineers for a long time—the windows. During the descent from the parent craft to the moon, the astronauts needed maximum visibility in order to select a landing site free from boulders, fissures or craters that might wreck the vehicle. Early concepts of the LM pictured it as a bubble of tough, specially laminated glass, with clear visibility all around. When Grumman began actual work on the vehicle, however, it was soon realized that to provide so much glass was impossible; not only was that amount of glass too heavy, but it would overexpose the astronauts to the lunar sunlight, which can get as hot as 250° F. on the moon's surface. Summing up the problem, Howard Sherman, LM system engineer concerned with human factors such as visibility, said, "We knew we had to trade off visibility for thermal protection so we decided to figure out the smallest possible windows to fit the astronauts' needs."

Challenge of the windows

The original plan for the LM's cabin had the astronauts seated during the descent, each man facing two windows—a larger one about two feet directly in front of his eyes and a smaller one near his knees. The total area of the four windows was 13 square feet. But this design proved unsatisfactory; the windows still weighed too much and gave too much exposure to the sun. Moreover, with his eyes two feet from the larger window and even farther from the one at knee level, each seated astronaut would have only a limited field of vision. If the LM were to descend toward the landing site on a slant, the astronauts would have no direct view of the touchdown spot. If the descent were vertical, the area directly below the vehicle would be completely hidden.

For two years the engineers racked their brains trying to figure out a way to make the windows smaller while giving the astronauts a direct view along their descent path. At about the same time, they were puzzled by a related detail—the design of the astronauts' seats. And then one day in 1964, a casual remark provided the key that unlocked the solution to both the window and seat problems.

On that day a group of Grumman and NASA engineers were discussing the design and arrangement of equipment in the LM's cabin. One of the engineers complained that the astronauts' seats took up too much space and weight. George Franklin, a NASA engineer, pointed out that the LM's descent from the parent craft to the surface of the moon would take about an hour, or less. Was there any reason why the astronauts could not stand upright in the cabin for that short trip? Seats were not really necessary.

Once it was agreed that the seats could go, the window dilemma just about solved itself. Standing instead of seated, the astronauts would have their eyes close to the windows, and each window then need not be bigger than a man's face.

Complications in a simple solution

Although the answer to the problem of seats and windows turned out to be simple enough, revising the LM's cabin to accommodate the changes was another story. Since altering any one cabin feature affected many other features, each of which then had to be redesigned and retested, the job required the efforts of no less than seven major engineering groups at Grumman. For example, with the astronauts in an upright position, control panels had to be rearranged so that the instruments would still be within convenient reach. Also, the standing position created a brand-new problem—devising a harness to protect the men during the landing. Padded, reclining seats would have minimized the danger, but now a special restraining rig had to be developed to keep the astronauts from being tossed about at the instant of impact. Finally, the collective work of the seven engineering groups produced a safe and seatless cabin. It had two small triangular windows whose total area was less than four square feet and whose visibility was far better than that provided by the previous 13 square feet of laminated glass. Both windows were pitched inward at the bottom so that the astronauts could look straight down as they approached their landing site.

How vital was the design of the windows—and how thorough the systems engineers had been in developing the LM in its entirety—became startlingly clear on the first moon landing, when astronaut Armstrong took control of the LM and picked his way to a safe landing spot away from the computer-set target, which turned out to be a rock-filled crater. Had he not had a sufficiently clear view of the boulders below, and of the safe spot nearby a minute before the fuel ran out; had he not had an engine he could throttle and turn; had he not had a vehicle that could hover and tilt, Armstrong might never have radioed back one of the most historic statements to be heard from space: "Tranquillity Base here. The Eagle has landed."

Education without End

Until the late 18th Century, engineering was more a trade than a profession, a set of mechanical skills passed from father to son, from master to apprentice. There was no such thing as a school for engineers until 1794, when the Ecole Polytechnique was established in Paris. The first comparable American engineering school, Rensselaer Polytechnic Institute, was founded 30 years later. In recent years 269 colleges in the U.S. have awarded annually some 39,000 bachelor degrees in engineering, 16,000 masters degrees and 3,000 doctorates to meet the demands of technology.

At schools such as Massachusetts Institute of Technology *(opposite)*, entering freshmen, who already know more science than the practicing engineer of 50 years ago, are intensively trained in scientific concepts of engineering rather than in mechanical techniques which may be outmoded in a short time. On a broad base of mathematics, chemistry, physics and the humanities are laid specialized studies in such fields as electronics, metallurgy and architecture. Even after he graduates, the engineer will continue to study. For the engineer—like the scientist—can never know enough.

THE FUTURE ENGINEERS
Students hurry across the plaza to their classes at Massachusetts Institute of Technology. M.I.T. undergraduates are usually pressed for time. The school subjects its 7,400 students, hand-picked from almost every state in the union and 84 countries, to one of the toughest curricula in the world; as a consequence its engineering graduates are among the world's best-trained.

A Stress on Science

Not many years ago it was said that only a handful of men in the world understood Einstein's complex theory of relativity. Today at M.I.T. it is taught to freshmen (*below*) as part of an intensive year of education in science. For most engineering students, the accent on science had begun in high school; a large fraction of M.I.T.'s freshmen have already acquired a strong background in calculus, physics and chemistry.

The freshman science courses at M.I.T., and at most other engineering schools, are far more advanced than those that are taught at liberal arts colleges. Although some of the basic lectures are delivered to as many as 500 freshmen at a time, they are supplemented by the teaching of small groups by eminent faculty members, by seminars and by opportunities to work on research projects. Thus, a freshman may find himself talking about stroboscopic light with Professor Harold Edgerton, the inventor of the stroboscope, or considering whether quasars are giant pulsars with Professor Philip Morrison, a noted atomic physicist who for the last 10 years has concerned himself with astronomy and cosmology.

The emphasis in these freshman courses is always on scientific theory —the *why* of science, not just the *how*. Lectures, exercises, demonstrations and laboratory work alike are designed to make a student think through a problem rather than arrive at a prescribed solution. This is essentially the way an engineer will use science throughout his career.

A PRACTICAL PROBLEM

In a freshman chemistry laboratory, two students attempt to measure the reaction rate of an organic compound with alcohol in order to determine the energy changes involved. The objective of such experiments is not to attain exact figures—results often vary—but to introduce students to a wide range of chemical concepts. All M.I.T. freshmen are required to take a class that involves laboratory work.

TWO APPROACHES TO PHYSICS

Explaining gravitation to a lecture group of 400 freshmen, Professor Anthony French indicates a chalked equation. On the blackboard over his head is part of a relativity formula. This intensive physics course consumes 12 hours per week: five in the classroom (three lectures and two discussion periods) and seven in "outside preparation"—i.e., homework. Freshmen must also take similar courses in mathematics and chemistry and are encouraged to seek more information from the faculty, who are readily accessible to students after classes *(above)*.

89

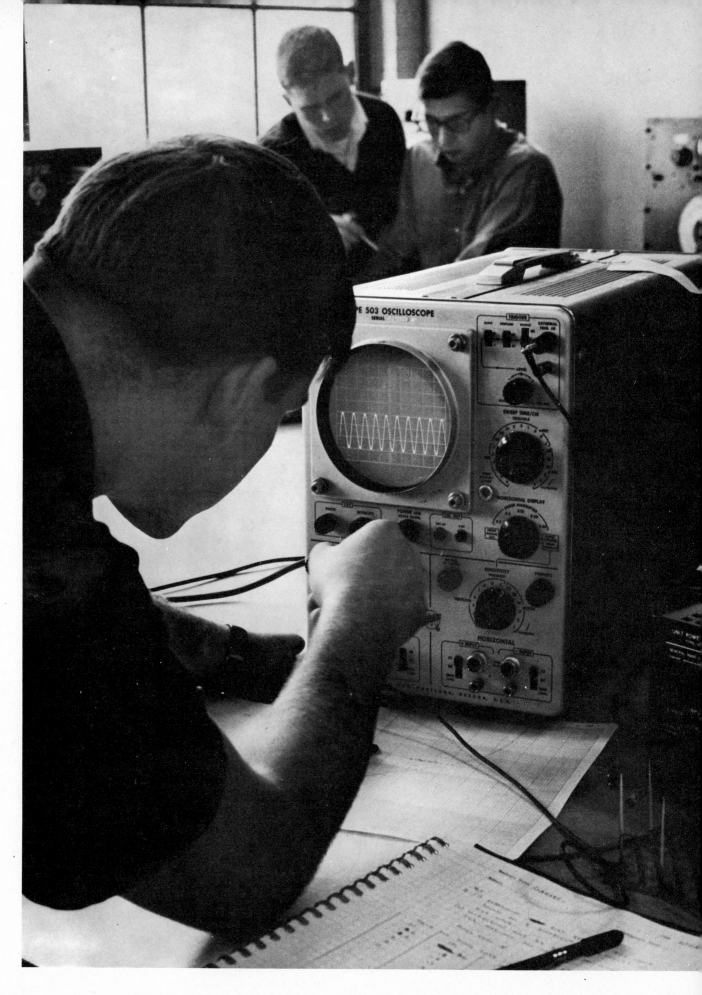

From Op Art
to Oscilloscope

Not until the end of his freshman year does an M.I.T. student consider the selection of his specialized field of engineering. His choice is wide. At M.I.T., engineering is broken down into eight groupings: civil, mechanical, metallurgical, electrical, chemical, aeronautical and astronautical, marine, and nuclear. But within each grouping are subdivisions encompassing virtually every type of engineering that is practiced today. Students may sample several of these fields through specially devised interdisciplinary courses; the students building structural models below, for example, must combine elements of engineering and architecture. For those who have already decided on a specialty, there are important tools to be mastered *(left)* before advanced work is attempted.

Most engineering schools attempt to broaden their students' education by offering liberal arts courses to supplement the technical curriculum. M.I.T. requires its students to take such courses in all eight semesters, and has pioneered an integrated humanities course—combining such subjects as philosophy, art and history. The idea is to produce a rounded engineer, equally familiar with op art *(right)* or an oscilloscope.

SPOTS BEFORE HIS EYES
Freshman Barry Unger peers at the spotted reflection in his glasses in order to get a different perspective on the painting behind him, part of an op art exhibit in M.I.T.'s library building.

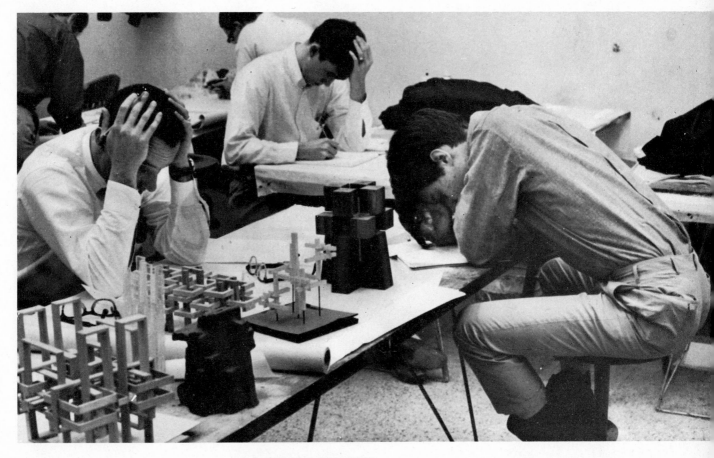

A TOOL FOR AN ENGINEER
Manipulating the controls of an oscilloscope for the first time, an M.I.T. sophomore gets acquainted with a basic electronic tool. Before tackling practical electronics projects, he must master this and a dozen other devices such as a digital voltmeter and wave-form generator.

AN EXERCISE IN ESTHETICS
Deep in thought, students in M.I.T.'s Form and Design class build models based on abstract visual and architectural concepts. A typical exercise requires the use of the number 36 as a construction theme. This architectural course is open to engineering students, who learn to consider the esthetic possibilities of form and space in designing various types of structures.

Feeding data into a specially programmed computer, an M.I.T. student researcher works on a Project MAC study of artificial intelligence.

Meshing Men and Machines

Today the electronic computer is as important a tool for the engineer as the sliderule, and every up-to-date school of engineering owns one. At M.I.T., however, the student does not go to the computer with his problems; the computer goes to him. Scattered around the campus are 250 typewriterlike machines that are the input-output stations of a multiple access computer. Any 30 of these stations can be used simultaneously and the student engineers often keep the computer clicking far into the night. M.I.T. also houses federally sponsored Project MAC (Multiple Access Computer), which includes a secondary system for feeding drawings, as well as data, into a computer.

Once they become proficient in the use of the computer, students can begin to undertake increasingly involved problems in systems analysis that can lead to such beneficial projects as the one shown below—a computerized study of the little-understood blood pressure control system.

The computer will return its neatly typed answers in a matter of seconds.

ENGINEERING AND MEDICINE
Analyzing the circulatory systems of animals with the help of a computer was a joint project of M.I.T. electrical engineers and medical researchers at Boston's Massachusetts General Hospital. This systems-engineering approach was used to make a study of blood pressure.

Mating Theory with Technique

"Now we use knowledge, not equipment," is the way one M.I.T. student describes the emphasis on theory in engineering education today. But engineers—and engineering students—are still builders. They still get their hands dirty.

Beginning with their sophomore year, M.I.T. students are assigned projects in their specialized fields. Although these are intended primarily as lessons in applied theory, they often serve a practical purpose as well. One such project produced a device that helps the blind to walk a straight line: a gyroscopic mechanism taps the fingers when the user veers to the right or left.

Projects undertaken on a graduate level, like the ones shown here, are usually more complex and are aimed at solving specific problems. It is in tasks like these, mostly supported by fellowships or grants from M.I.T., the federal government and private industry, that the fledgling engineer combines theory and technique in the most important test of his skills.

A REFRIGERATION PROJECT
An apparatus to test the cooling properties of Freon receives its finishing touches from Andrew Dickson, a graduate mechanical engineering student from South Africa. The project was sponsored by the American Society of Heating Engineers in an effort to develop cooling systems that would be suitable for atomic reactors.

WATCHING A WHIRLYBIRD

In a project supported by a grant from the United States Navy, Michael Scully and John Thompson closely examine the performance of a helicopter rotor as part of their work in the department of aeronautical and astronautical engineering. They expect the project to show a way to reduce helicopter noise, which is created chiefly by the rotor's whirling blades.

SAMPLING THE SOIL

Working in an M.I.T. laboratory, Herb Herrmann, a graduate student in civil engineering, studies soil samples taken from the banks of the Panama Canal. The United States Atomic Energy Commission underwrote the project as part of its study of the feasibility of using nuclear devices to excavate a sea-level canal in Panama that would speed ships in transit.

An Exchange
of Engineers

Scattered throughout the informally dressed student body at M.I.T. are small groups of older, conservatively dressed men who could easily be mistaken for professors. They, too, are students. One is the chief engineer of a washing machine company, 16 years out of college. Another, who has had his doctorate in physics for 13 years, works for a firm that makes computers. A third is a Navy captain engaged in the space program.

These men are part of a growing number of practicing engineers, many regarded as leaders in their fields, who return to engineering schools for refresher courses. Each of them recognizes the need of modern engineers to keep abreast of the latest developments in their own and related fields, and the college classroom is often the best place for them to get this information.

These middle-aged students represent one side of an informal exchange program between campus and industry. While veteran engineers return to class, youthful undergraduates are being sent out to study engineering in the field. Thus the theory and the practice of engineering are becoming more and more closely allied—a necessity in an era when scientific and technological change can make the most advanced knowledge obsolete in a decade, or even in a single year.

FATHER AND SON
Paul Rosen, Northeastern class of 1953, sits beside his son Mark, M.I.T. class of 1967, during a course in principles of transistors. The father, who was an electronics engineer at M.I.T.'s Lincoln Laboratory, returned to the classroom for a year to study new developments in his field.

ENGINEERS IN THE CLASSROOM
At M.I.T.'s Center for Advanced Engineering Study, Professor Arthur C. Smith teaches a course in electrical engineering to a class of practicing engineers. There are usually 20 to 30 such men on the campus (eventually up to 100 will be accommodated). They are chosen by their employers to spend a year there, studying the latest knowledge in their specialized fields.

STUDENTS IN THE FIELD
Working on a field project to improve the manufacture of sulfa drugs, three M.I.T. graduate students in chemical engineering observe closely at an American Cyanamid plant in New Jersey. A resident engineer *(far left)* explains one of the production steps as a technician demonstrates.

A New Crop
of Engineers

Final examinations are regarded as something of an anticlimax at most engineering schools. Months earlier, graduating seniors have had to make a decision either to remain in the academic world and work toward a master's degree or to enter the labor market immediately. By exam time, prospective employers have sent recruiting agents, sometimes referred to as ivory hunters by the students, to campuses around the country. At M.I.T. an average senior may consider several offers before making up his mind. However, most seniors—as many as 60 per cent in recent years—delay taking a job until after a year or more of graduate study.

A survey of M.I.T.'s class of 1970 shows trends typical of engineering schools today. Of the 323 graduates in engineering that year, nearly half —137—had specialized in electrical engineering, the normal prerequisite for working in the exacting aerospace and electronics industries. The remainder were distributed among the seven other major fields; for example, 22 took degrees in civil engineering, 19 in chemical engineering.

AT TESTING TIME
Written examinations at any school of engineering symbolize only the end of classroom studies; the real test comes later, in the laboratories and on the job. Here, 300 students take an examination in M.I.T.'s huge gymnasium, the latecomers overflowing onto the bleacher seats.

5
Skyscrapers, Radomes and Chips

Working under tight restrictions in the 23-square-mile area of Manhattan, engineers have built some 200 skyscrapers in 20 years.

TWO RADICAL DEVELOPMENTS distinguish the Old Man of long ago from the professional engineer of today. One is The Tool—the electronic computer—which enables him to calculate so closely that he can avoid cut-and-try experimentation. The other is The Method—systems engineering—which enables him to coordinate and plan projects that would have flabbergasted any Old Man, no matter how gifted. By using The Tool and The Method together, the modern engineer finds new forms of expression for his genius. His achievements are thus different from those of the Old Man not only in their size and complexity, but also in their character.

Three examples illustrate the great variety of the modern engineer's achievements. One is a building—the Pan Am Building, a massive commercial office building that was erected on one of the nation's busiest locations. Another is a defense weapon that is so diffuse it can scarcely be described: it is the vast network of communications lines and radomes that helps guard the United States against missile attack, the Ballistic Missile Early Warning System. The third fulfills a requirement that no Old Man could ever have conceived and is even smaller than the period at the end of this sentence: this is the transistor, the chip of electronic crystal on which much of future technology will be based.

New York City's Pan Am Building, rising 808 feet from the taxi-laden street to the helicopter-landing pad on its roof, is a major accomplishment in every sense. It is more than 10 times taller than the original height of the Sumerian ziggurat at Ur and encloses five times more space than the cathedral of Notre Dame in Paris. Its statistics are dazzling: it contains 60 acres of offices and 17,000 permanent workers—plus the 250,000 or so people who visit or pass through the building every day. The 59 floors are served by 18 moving stairways and 65 elevators, some of which shoot upward at 25 feet a second. The building uses 2,000 gallons of water every minute and as much electricity and telephone service as 10,000 homes. To allow for telephone demands, in fact, the New York Telephone Company had to install an $11-million, city-sized centralized exchange—the first ever devised for one building—with 1,000 tons of equipment on the 21st and part of the 20th floors.

This kind of forethought was dictated by the building's site, for the location required nothing less than an engineering monument. The Pan Am Building sits directly north of the mammoth Grand Central Terminal, the intersection point of two railroad and three subway lines connecting with two thirds of the New York metropolitan area. Because the commuting is so convenient, all the adjacent city blocks are jammed with large buildings providing working space for a quarter of a million people, as well as scores of restaurants to feed them lunch and dozens of hotels to house their out-of-town visitors. This exceptional concentration of existing office buildings and their life-giving traffic created unprecedented difficulties for Pan Am's engineers. The building could be constructed within an economical span of time only by the careful application of the principles of systems engineering: advance planning of the smallest details, rigid scheduling of each step, stern monitoring of the schedules and skillful execution of all operations.

Erecting the Pan Am Building was first of all an immense problem in structural engineering. The structural engineer, James Ruderman, was an obvious choice for this project. He had already planned a dozen of the buildings along Park Avenue north of the site—in fact was responsible for structural planning on about half of all the high-rise office construction in Manhattan since World War II. His first job was to decide where and how such a building could be put up without disrupting train service in the terminal underneath it or the heavy flow of pedestrian and automobile traffic around it. Ruderman, who died in 1966, three years after the job was completed, decided to erect his skyscraper on a site then occupied by an old six-story structure called the Grand Central Office Building, even though this choice meant he had to forgo a basement that rested on solid ground. Instead, his ground floor, like that of the Grand Central Office Building, would have to float above the two subterranean railroad track levels. The lower level of tracks, for suburban commuter trains, is on bedrock. The upper level, for long-distance expresses, is carried on a steel viaduct structure.

A foundation fitted into a maze

Ruderman noted without enthusiasm that the Grand Central Office Building's foundation footings, which he would use for some of his building's supports, were continuations of the railroad tracks' viaduct columns, instead of resting independently on the lower level's bedrock. The vibrations of the express trains would be carried from the viaduct through the footings and up into the building. He would have to overcome that vibration, as well as adding 99 new foundation footings for the skyscraper tower. The new footings would have to be carried down into the bedrock between the tracks on both levels—without interfering with the heavy daily train traffic on the tracks. Ruderman also realized that building immediately above the railroad tracks meant that high-speed elevators could not receive passengers on the street floor lobby; there would be no basement under the elevator shafts for bumper space. His solution was to have passengers enter the elevators on the second floor, which they would reach on moving stairways.

After Ruderman figured out where in the maze of underground railroad tracks he could locate his foundation columns, he turned his specifications over to the architect, Richard Roth of Emery Roth and Sons. Roth and the developer, the late Erwin S. Wolfson, worked out a design for a 50-story rectangular building with three million square feet of rental space. Such a massive building promised attractive financial returns in rents, but it posed a great problem: it was not right for the site. In an area already filled with modern, glass-walled buildings, the planners wanted to create a building with a distinctive character—one that would break up the "canyon" effect of the rows of buildings on the avenue and one that would attract a major corporation as a tenant.

Roth and Wolfson brought in as design consultants the distinguished architects, Walter Gropius and Pietro Belluschi. They designed a slim, octagonal tower; its narrow width on the east and west would allow plenty of sunlight to infiltrate around it. But this design had only 1.5 million square feet of rental space. A more spacious compromise was worked out, enlarging the base building to 10 stories, raising the total height to 59 stories and thickening the octagonal tower.

The construction of the building involved more than 200 engineers supervising 7,500 craftsmen from 75 different trades. Ruderman encountered little difficulty sinking the foundation footings and columns between and around the railroad tracks, although in some places the 20½-inch-wide columns had to be squeezed into spaces that were only 24 inches wide. But as he had anticipated, keeping the vibration of underground trains from shaking the building was a serious problem. He wanted to use the old Grand Central Office Building foundation columns, which rested on the express train level's viaduct, to support the 10-story base building. He solved the vibration problem here by leaving some of the old columns to support the building's wide lobby area, where there would be no tenants and where the vibration would not cause much annoyance. The remaining columns, under the tenant areas, were sheared off, insulation inserted to cut off the vibration, and new columns spliced on at the ground-floor level.

Taming turbulent winds

The helicopter port on top of the building, which makes possible quick air transportation from the heart of Manhattan to the city's three main airports, was an afterthought, planned when the original design of the structure was already completed. An extra 300 tons of steel was added to the framework from the 20th floor up to support the 12-inch-thick concrete landing pad. This structural change was simple enough, but overcoming the turbulent winds that howl around the top of the skyscraper was not so easy. The problem was solved by erecting wind-deflecting aluminum vanes around the edges of the roof. The vanes divert gusts upward and blend them into a steady breeze 35 to 45 feet above the landing pad, where they cause no trouble.

The problems of location that make the Pan Am Building a unique engineering achievement could hardly be more different from those that faced the engineers of the Ballistic Missile Early Warning System, called BMEWS (and pronounced "bemuse"). Yet, again it was the site—in this

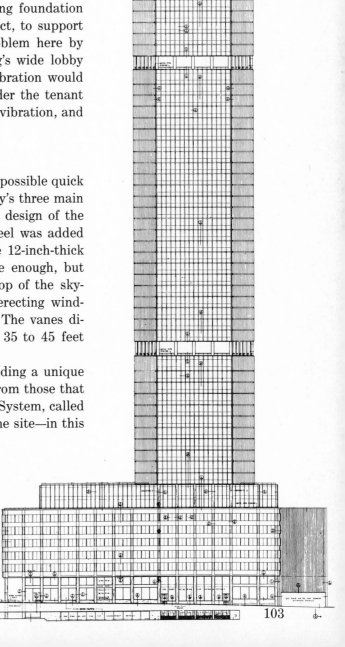

THE PAN AM BUILDING in New York City, one of the world's largest commercial office structures, presented its engineers with an unusual problem: building a 59-floor skyscraper above 26 underground tracks of Grand Central Terminal without disturbing the busy railroad operation. Engineers not only solved the problem by precise scheduling, but finished the entire building in just over two years —complete with a heliport on the roof.

case its remoteness and its Arctic cold—that transformed a difficult challenge into an almost impossible one.

BMEWS is an electronic fence designed to detect enemy long-range ballistic missiles within minutes after their launching from sites on the other side of the world. All BMEWS can do is sound the alarm. And because of the missiles' speed, it can give the alarm only 15 minutes before they reach their targets. BMEWS' brief warning, however, is sufficient to permit the immediate launching of retaliatory missiles, and it can thus deter an attack.

If an intercontinental missile is launched somewhere in Eastern Europe or Asia, and spotted by BMEWS radar, computers immediately begin to figure out its range, direction and speed. The radar keeps watching the approaching projectile while more computers decide where it came from, what it is aimed at and when it should land on its target. This information is fed into coding machines and transferred in the form of a coded message carried over both radio and wire communication links, which flash it in a quick sound signal—not much more than an instantaneous "beep." This goes to the Combat Operations Center of the North American Air Defense Command in Colorado, where it is decoded and immediately marked on a huge electronic map. Other communication tie-ins feed the information to the rest of the U.S. defense system and to bases and command posts in England and Canada. The whole process, from the first spotting of the missile to the outlining of its route and probable target on the map, takes less than half a minute.

The building of BMEWS was a one-billion-dollar job accomplished against rigid time and cost deadlines, and is the world's biggest concentration of electronics equipment devoted to a single operation. The Air Force awarded the prime contract to the Radio Corporation of America, which divided the work among 2,900 subcontractors and appointed as the program manager a Cornell-educated electrical engineer, Dyer Brainerd Holmes, who had already earned a reputation for big-league engineering triumphs. Holmes was faced with the assignment of setting up three sites for radar detection and tracking equipment: one at Thule in Greenland, near an older Arctic air base, another at Clear in Alaska and a third at Fylingdales Moor in England, a few miles from a watchtower built 17 centuries earlier to give the Romans warning of enemy attack.

Missiles, oranges or card tables

Holmes encountered enormous construction troubles at Thule. More than 700 engineers, technicians and skilled workmen had to install four huge detection radar antennas, one revolving 110-ton tracking radar, and provide electronic gear, power plants and repair shops, along with specifications for all buildings, including living quarters and recreation facilities for a permanent party of 1,000 men. The detection radar antennas are shaped like drive-in movie screens but each is 400 feet long and 165 feet high, the size of a 40-story building tipped on its side. This antenna simply searches for objects rising in the sky, its probing radar beam sweeping continuously back and forth. The BMEWS radar is said to be delicate enough to spot an orange thrown into the air 1,500 miles away. A few years ago, a yarn was circulated about a similar detection device, which had an excited Coast Guard radarman reporting a sighting of four submarine periscopes in the Gulf Stream off the coast of Florida. It turned out that he had spotted a floating card table with its four legs extended upward.

When the huge detection radar senses an unidentified object, a "bogie," in the sky, it automatically aims a separate tracking radar at it. The tracker then follows the bogie, while computers measure its range, direction and speed, and estimate when and where it will hit. The tracking antenna is a dish 84 feet across which is swept around after its prey by hydraulic motors. It is protected against the violent weather of the Arctic by a huge fiber glass sphere, called a radome, that sits on top of a three-story building filled with electronic gear. The whole affair, which extends 15 stories from ground to radome top, resembles a gigantic golf ball resting on a flat rectangle as large as a city block. These high antennas and tracking dishes had to be reinforced to resist the 185-mile-an-hour winds that are possible at Thule, which is only 927 miles from the North Pole. While they were being built, heated huts were located at intervals along the roads so that men caught in a sudden 40-below-zero gale could run for shelter to keep from freezing. Even so, most of the winter work on the Thule installation had to be done inside big heated tents so the men would not have to wear the cumbersome thermal suits that must be put on before going out of doors in the Arctic cold.

Cooling the frozen North

Construction engineers putting up buildings and radar devices on the Arctic ice met unique problems. The radar had to stay steady in one fixed position although the permafrost under it, hundreds of feet thick, shifts if it begins to melt. Curiously enough, in that sub-zero climate, refrigerating pipes had to be sunk into the permafrost below some buildings. Heat from the buildings would melt the supporting ground unless it was kept artificially frozen, and the melting would cause the building and its radar equipment to settle unevenly.

The cold and remoteness made even simple matters of delivery disproportionately complex. For example, a shipment of components that were extremely sensitive to temperature changes and so delicately made that they could be damaged by any sudden jolt or vibration, had to be shifted from the Thule air base to the radar site, a trip of 13 miles over rough roads and in freezing weather. A moving van, air-conditioned and with special hydraulic shockproof springs, was flown to Thule from the U.S. just to do that one job. Most of the heavy equipment and supplies sent to Thule went by ship, which called for tight scheduling and around-the-clock unloading because the harbor at Thule is free from ice for only 10 weeks in the summer. When the freeze began to come in September 1958, the engineers answered an urgent appeal for an extra few weeks of unloading time by rigging compressed-air tubes in the water around the docks. The bubbles from the tubes held off the formation of ice for an added month.

Despite the magnitude of these difficulties, Holmes saw BMEWS finished on schedule and within the estimated costs. It worked perfectly—as it turned out, almost too well. One night in October 1960, the radar at Thule picked up an unidentified object in the sky somewhere beyond the North Pole. The defense command at Colorado was signaled. But could it really be an attack? Since the system was still in its early experimental stage, this was very difficult to decide, particularly since the radar was supplying no apparent track for the object. There was just something "out there." Finally an outlandish possibility occurred to the technicians: perhaps the powerful radars had hit the rising moon, 240,000 miles away, and bounced back. That was exactly what had happened.

Small, simple and significant

Huge BMEWS and the even vaster defense system of which it is a part depend entirely on another engineering achievement, one that is small in physical size but great in significance. Building BMEWS would not have been practical without the transistor, which most people know only from the portable radios and tape recorders that it made possible. A transistor is a simple device for switching electricity on or off and for amplifying weak currents into strong ones—essential tasks in giant computers as well as in pocket radios. It is small, it needs little power for operation, and it does not heat up. But most important of all, a modern transistor is reliable, and that is why it is so essential to BMEWS. Each of the BMEWS computers contains so many components that if old-style vacuum tubes had to be used instead of transistors the computer would always be shut down for repairs because one or more tubes would always be burned out.

The vital reliability of the transistor was provided by engineers. As a result of their work—many different men in many laboratories were involved—a high-grade transistor will theoretically continue to function forever unless it is damaged.

The magnitude of this achievement becomes plainer with close examination of the transistor itself. If you look inside a pocket radio you will see six to 10 metal cans, each about the size of a pea. Inside each can is a transistor, a shiny gray chip one tenth the size of a pinhead and usually made from the common element silicon. To begin with, that silicon was perhaps the purest substance ever refined, certainly the purest ever made for large-scale commercial use. It contains impurities of only one part in three billion. Then that superpure silicon was deliberately dirtied. With dazzling precision a few atoms of impurities were added in specific amounts and at specific positions within the silicon to regulate the behavior of the transistor. Manufacturing one, an engineer has said, "is like solving a three-dimensional crossword puzzle the size of a pinpoint—only instead of letters we use atoms to spell out the right combinations."

The engineering techniques that accomplish this feat depend first on absolute cleanliness, far more rigorous than that of any hospital surgery, since unwanted impurities can destroy a transistor. Technicians are capped, gowned, even booted. Air is filtered and washed repeatedly; it is also pressurized so that it flows outward when a door is opened, thus keeping dust-filled air from entering the "clean room."

Cleanliness protects the transistor, but it is made by engineering artists displaying to the full their knowledge of the way atoms move about in solids, liquids and gases as temperatures change. To start, pure crystals of silicon are melted and a desired impurity, called a "dopant," is added. From the doped pot of molten silicon, a single crystal can be grown by dipping and withdrawing a "seed" rod of silicon, so that molten material solidifies on the seed. As the crystal is pulled from the molten silicon, the dopant is distributed throughout its length. In this way, silicon of varying electronic properties, depending on the tapering-off of the dopant, can be obtained from one crystal rod.

The rod of silicon—looking like a blued and purpled straight steel sausage—is sliced into thin wafers. Each wafer, already doped with one kind of impurity, is given a .00006-inch-thick coating of silicon containing yet another impurity. This is accomplished by "baking" the wafer in a high-temperature reaction chamber filled with a silicon gas containing the desired dopant. After several similar treatments, the wafer is finished. Only about an inch across, it will be cut into 1,000 transistor chips—an operation that, because the chips are so infinitesimal, must be monitored by a skilled operator watching through a microscope.

Machines to operate machines

Such virtuoso engineering has made possible the reliable transistor and the related devices that sprang from its development. And they in turn are bringing about the Second Industrial Revolution, the age of automatic control in which machines are no longer operated by men but by other machines. This revolution is already farther along than most people realize, but a hint of its significance can be gained from a story of its beginnings. A few years ago Eugene Ayres, a retired chemical engineer, told of a group of engineers asked to design a $50-million oil refinery for an Asian government. Their plan called for a complex array of machinery with many automatic controls, as most oil refineries are set up nowadays. The government, which had an embarrassing abundance of unemployed manpower in its country, asked the Americans to eliminate all the automation and to revise the plant so that it could be handled entirely by employed help. After considerable study, the engineers decided that the oil could not be refined by human operators, no matter how skilled they might be. It was not a question of efficiency or operating costs. With men instead of automatic controls guiding the machinery, a modern oil refinery cannot run at all.

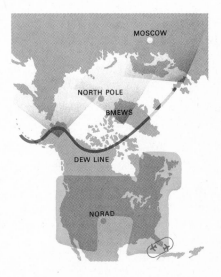

A VAST RADAR NETWORK protects most of North America against enemy bombers and missiles. The most farflung of its sentinels are those of BMEWS (Ballistic Missile Early Warning System). Devised by systems engineers, BMEWS scans the northern approaches from installations in Alaska, Greenland and England; each station is equipped with trackers that can spot a missile 3,000 miles away and report it within seconds to NORAD (North American Air Defense Command) headquarters in Colorado. BMEWS is backed by some 40 trackers in the DEW (Distant Early Warning) Line, 67 U.S. radar stations and radar-equipped patrol planes.

107

The Challenge
of a Great Bridge

The Verrazano-Narrows Bridge, vaulting 6,690 feet across the entrance to New York Harbor, dramatizes the engineer's goal: to meet a practical need by overcoming problems of terrain, space and materials with a structure that combines function, grace and economy. The bridge's deceptively simple design reflects six years of planning by scores of engineers in many fields. Their talents produced a $305-million bridge that is massive in conception, yet so delicately engineered that its parts fit with tolerances as fine as those of a watch.

The chief designer was the dean of American bridge builders, the late Othmar H. Ammann, who was responsible for the George Washington and other great bridges. Under his guidance the entire bridge was first meticulously preconstructed on paper. The blueprints encompassed every detail, from the depth of excavations to the height of towers, from the shape of each span segment to the placement of the more than six million rivets. The result was a grand design for one of the world's longest and highest suspension bridges, a design so precise that engineers considered the job half-finished when workmen appeared at the site, in 1959.

THE END IN SIGHT
Viewed from its base, one of the bridge's towers looms skyward, ready to receive the final segment of the main span. Like the pieces of a jigsaw puzzle, each structural element of the Verrazano is unique and has a precise relationship to all the others. The roadway sections, for example, were designed to intermesh, but with space for expansion or contraction due to changing temperatures.

THE BROOKLYN APPROACH

A giant loop of concrete leads traffic on and off the Brooklyn-Long Island side of the bridge. Before the Verrazano bridge opened, motorists traveling between central New Jersey and Long Island had to go through the heart of New York City, a longer and more congested route. The bridge has also opened Staten Island—formerly linked to the rest of the city only by ferries —to residential and commercial development.

110

New Routes for Teeming Traffic

The basic reason for the Verrazano-Narrows Bridge was simple: logic demanded it. The shortest route between the Northeast and the middle Atlantic states cuts across Long Island and Staten Island to New Jersey. The unbridged Narrows between Brooklyn and Staten Island was an offense to all right-thinking traffic engineers—as is the one gap still remaining: the eastern end of Long Island Sound, where a bridge could join New England and Long Island.

The need for the Verrazano was dramatically demonstrated from the day it opened, November 21, 1964. In its first year 17,116,000 vehicles, five million more than had been estimated, crossed the span. When Long Island Sound is finally bridged, completing the tie to New England, traffic on the Verrazano may increase greatly. But by then an additional deck will have been opened to handle the load.

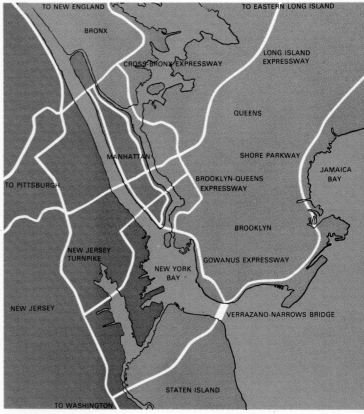

CLOSING THE GAP
The Verrazano and its adjoining arteries on Staten Island and Long Island are boons to thousands of motorists bound for innumerable destinations. The map shows how the bridge fits into the complex of highways that convey motorists into and around the nation's largest metropolis.

A NIGHTTIME PANORAMA
The traffic flows across the brightly illuminated Verrazano bridge and its approaches. Stretching out in the distance is the new Staten Island Expressway, cutting through Staten Island and leading to the Goethals Bridge, the New Jersey Turnpike and the cities to the south and west.

Supports Piercing Sky and Earth

The Verrazano's 693-foot twin towers, rising from the waters of New York Bay, betray little of their complex anatomy or the careful planning that preceded their construction. Of primary importance was the nature of the subsoil on which they rest.

Meticulous investigations were undertaken to determine the most efficient foundations—either steel pilings drilled directly into rock or platforms embedded deep in the subsoil above rock. Because the rock stratum at the Brooklyn site lay too deep, platforms were decided on. Then, to achieve lightness and strength, the engineers built the towers out of prefabricated hollow steel cells—10,000 in all—stacked tier upon tier. This sturdy design enables the towers to support 170,000 tons of roadway and cable—and to transmit this immense load, and the towers' own combined weight of 54,000 tons, to the foundations.

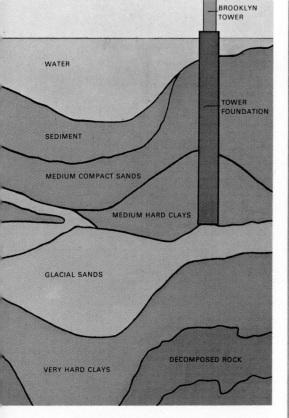

WATER

SEDIMENT

MEDIUM COMPACT SANDS

MEDIUM HARD CLAYS

GLACIAL SANDS

VERY HARD CLAYS

DECOMPOSED ROCK

BROOKLYN TOWER

TOWER FOUNDATION

FOOTING BENEATH THE NARROWS
The engineers determined the nature of the river bottom by drilling into the earth layers at the tower sites. This profile of the Brooklyn side shows that thick layers of sand and clay had to be penetrated to reach, at 170 feet, a material unyielding enough to bear the tower's weight. The base of the other tower rests at 105 feet.

WORK IN PROGRESS
Beginning to rise on its pedestals, the Staten Island tower receives a cell section from the "creeper" crane moving up and down on tracks between the legs. The boxlike cells formed a maze so complex that workers inside the towers used charts so as not to lose their way.

A TRIUMPHANT ARCH
Soaring as high as a 70-story skyscraper, the Staten Island tower nears completion. Set almost a mile from each other, the two towers, though seemingly parallel, are an inch and five eighths farther apart at their summits than at their bases, because of the earth's curvature.

PLATFORMS IN THE SKY
A pair of catwalks of wood and wire mesh joins the Brooklyn tower to its anchorage and its haze-enshrouded mate near Staten Island. The catwalks were working platforms for the men who tied down the cable wires, a job that took the bridge workers more than five months.

113

A Crossing Made on Threads of Steel

The Verrazano's deck is suspended from four cables; compressed within them is enough wire to reach more than halfway to the moon—143,000 miles of pencil-thick wire that required three years to produce. In all, there are 104,432 individual threads of steel reaching from shore to shore.

Planning the cables was an exacting task. Not only did the weight of the roadway have to be considered; changing weather was important too. The bridge was designed so that in a gale the cables sway, bowing out the span as much as 14 feet; heated by the summer sun the cables stretch, lowering the span as much as six feet below its highest arc, reached in the winter when the cables contract.

LAUNCHING THE WIRES

At the Brooklyn anchorage a shuttling wheel begins its journey across the Narrows, pulling two loops of wire from a drum on shore. Each wire is capable of supporting three and a half tons. When 428 wires were laid, they were gathered into a strand, 61 strands per cable.

OVER THE MAIN SPAN

As the wheel reaches the top of the Staten Island tower, a worker pulls down the wires to place them in their guide slots *(left foreground)*. Two wheels ran simultaneously day and night, as teams of workers competed to see which could lay down the most wire in a single shift.

114

ONE JOURNEY ENDED

At the Staten Island anchorage a bridge worker clamps the wires into a strand *(above)*. Between the anchorages the strands were compressed into cables three feet thick, but here the strands are individually attached to eyebars. Men at the mooring *(below)* remove the loops from the wheel and replace them with others from a supply drum for the return trip.

Designed for a Tug-of-War

Half-buried in the ground and largely hidden by approaches to the bridge, the huge anchorages to which the cables are moored are seldom noticed. Yet they had to be designed with the utmost care: these structures of reinforced concrete must resist the continuous 250-million-pound pull exerted by the cables and roadway of the bridge. Should either anchorage fail, the deck and the towers as well would plummet into the Narrows.

Embedded into each mooring are steel eyebars to which the cable wires are fixed. As additional strands were formed and attached to eyebars, more cement was poured into the anchorages to maintain a calculated counterpull against the increasing weight of the cables. The completed moorings have enormous bulk; each weighs 367,000 tons and at its base covers the area of two football fields side by side. Like the towers, they are based solidly in the subsoil. At a depth of 76 feet, test borings revealed an unyielding stratum for the base of the Staten Island anchorage; firm footing for its mate was reached at 52 feet.

CABLES LOCKED IN CONCRETE
From a saddle *(upper right)*, the strands of a cable flare out to their eyebars. Other eyebars *(foreground)* were embedded in the concrete as more strands were formed. The finished moorings are triangular, a shape designer Ammann found more pleasing than the usual rectangle.

A Roadway High in the Sky

With towers, cables and anchorages virtually complete, only one major task remained—adding the roadway. The 60-ton, double-decked roadway sections had to be hoisted from barges and attached to wire rope suspenders. Instead of starting on one side of the bridge and assembling the roadway straight across to the other side, the engineers began the deck at the center of the main span and extended it shoreward to meet the side spans. This procedure was necessary to maintain even weight distribution throughout the bridge. Although traffic engineers estimated that it would be 10 years before two decks were needed, Ammann placed both: wind tunnel tests revealed that the combined weight of twin decks plus the trusses between them would help stiffen the roadway against the wind.

THE FIRST SECTION
One segment of the 388-ton steel roadway is hoisted aloft from its barge and into position precisely in the center of the bridge, 228 feet above the Narrows. Each deck section was pre-assembled at a railroad yard five miles upriver and then floated to the construction site.

THE FINAL LINK
Slung from steel suspender ropes, the center span of the roadway (above) reaches toward the Brooklyn tower. In the picture at right, only a single segment remains to be placed. Its tongue will slip into the slot of the tower's wind bracket (foreground)—not snugly, but with enough free space to allow the span to swell and shrink as the temperature changes. Distorted by the camera angle, the bracket appears much larger than it is. The weight of the completed deck caused the cables' arc to sag nearly 28 feet, exactly as calculated by the designer.

Silhouetted against the evening sky and melting into the dusk, the completed bridge executes in steel and concrete Ammann's dream of

creating an "enormous object drawn as faintly as possible" and having an "ultimate simplicity of form and a clear expression of function."

6

Waste Not,
Want Not

Broken oyster shells ride a conveyor belt at a chemical plant in Freeport, Texas. A cheap, readily available source of calcium carbonate, the shells are used in an economical process devised by chemical engineers to get magnesium from seawater.

JAMES WATT is counted a great engineer, not for building the first steam engine—he did not—but for designing an economical one, a machine so efficient at converting fuel into useful power that it changed the structure of civilization. Henry Ford's fame, too, rests largely on his engineer's sense of frugality. Others had built automobiles before him; his Model T displaced the horse because it could supply dependable transportation at less cost than any beast. For the engineer is parsimonious. To him, something is worth doing only if it is useful, and it can be useful only if the value it returns is greater than the value it consumes.

The engineer's frugality may be just penny-pinching on a grand scale. The man who can redesign an engine part so that it costs a fraction of a cent less to manufacture is marked for promotion. The cumulative effect of such seemingly picayune savings, multiplied by the economies of mass production, can make the difference between an engine that is attractive to the buyer on a cost basis and one that is not. More dramatic in their impact are the large-scale savings that result from an engineering breakthrough. Aluminum, once enormously expensive, became cheap enough to wrap sandwiches because Charles Martin Hall devised an economical refining process.

Waste is intolerable to the engineer. Materials formerly discarded are today used in manufacturing: sulfur, at one time an annoying impurity, is now recovered at oil refineries; and wallboard, shingles and other building materials are made from the sugarcane fiber once discarded as waste. Low-yield ores such as iron-bearing taconite and low-grade copper, which miners considered worthless not many years ago, are today being profitably concentrated by new grinding and magnetic-extraction systems. Harmful minerals, blown out of smokestacks in the fumes from copper and lead smelters to settle on the surrounding countryside, once destroyed vegetation and livestock; now, filtered out of the fumes, these poisons provide large quantities of valuable arsenic.

Yet the engineer is no Scrooge. Getting the most from the least has a meaning that extends beyond the immediate costs of production. He seeks the effective exploitation of natural resources, trying always to consume less of them, and to draw what he does consume from the most plentiful supplies—the air, the sea, the widely distributed minerals. Today the engineer takes an ever-broader view of costs. In calculating the expense of strip-mining coal, he must also figure the need for later restoration of the gouged-out landscape; the estimate of a new automobile design allows for extra devices to purify exhaust gases and protect the atmosphere. In this sense the engineer's frugality has turned him into a conservationist: he continues to satisfy the practical needs of his society, but those engineering needs are now interpreted to include such intangibles as health, recreation space and natural beauty.

A single engineering advance can often promote economy—in several meanings of that word. A classic example of this kind of progress is the development of no-knock high-test gasoline for high-compression engines. Before World War I, Thomas Midgley Jr. and T. A. Boyd, both chemical engineers, applied themselves to this problem under the direction of the famed Boss Ket—Charles F. Kettering, inventor of the self-starter and for 27 years Director of Research for General Motors.

Kettering knew that an auto engine would produce more power with smaller fuel consumption if the gasoline in the cylinders were subjected to greater compression before it was ignited. The trouble was that the gasoline available at that time exploded too violently if ignited under high compression; these erratic, untimed explosions—called "knocks"—wasted power and could even wreck the engine. Kettering set Midgley and Boyd the task of concocting a no-knock gasoline—fuel that could be highly compressed and would explode evenly when it was ignited by the spark from the spark plug.

A clue from trailing arbutus

The solution of the knock problem was the result of accidental discoveries made during a series of tests that were logically designed but wrongly aimed. Reasoning from his knowledge that kerosene, which knocked more than gasoline, did not vaporize as readily as gasoline, Kettering had decided that there was a connection between knocking and low vaporization. This idea led him and Midgley to the incorrect notion that knocking was affected by heat absorption. They recalled that trailing arbutus, a wild flower with red-backed leaves, blooms under snow in the early spring. They then speculated that gasoline might absorb heat quicker and vaporize faster if it were dyed red.

The closest thing to a red dye available in the laboratory was iodine. With this addition, knocking was reduced, but further tests showed that the improvement was due to the chemical nature of iodine, not to its color. Iodine, however, was not a practical no-knock agent; it was too scarce and it damaged the fuel. But the test did show that knock could be suppressed by adding a chemical to the fuel.

The next try was with organic compounds resembling the dye aniline. With aniline in its gasoline, the compression in a Chevrolet's engine could be almost doubled and its mileage per gallon increased 40 per cent. But the smell of the car's exhaust was terrible. Further experiments with other compounds failed to turn up effective materials. Midgley became discouraged and wanted to give up the tests. Kettering, about to go to New York on a business trip, persuaded Midgley to wait until his return before calling a halt.

As Boyd tells the story in his biography of Kettering, *Professional Amateur*, the engineer saw a newspaper item about an attempt to make a universal solvent from a compound of selenium, a rare metal. Kettering's eye was attracted to the item, Boyd says, because it reminded him of his favorite joke about a skeptic who said to two chemists working on a universal solvent, "When you fellows get that stuff that will dissolve everything in the world, just what are you going to keep it in?"

Kettering clipped out the item and brought it back to Midgley and Boyd, suggesting that they try a selenium material. It turned out to be five times more powerful than any antiknock agent used previously; and further experiments showed that substances containing tellurium were four times more powerful than selenium. But the smell of tellurium compounds made the engine's exhaust even more unbearable than when aniline was mixed into the fuel. "The foul odor got into the men's systems and on their clothes," Boyd wrote. "They couldn't wash it off, for water only made the odor worse . . . anyone working with tellurium was virtually a social outcast."

Finally, in 1921, the search led to tetraethyl lead, now better known by its trade name, Ethyl, which was more effective than tellurium—and 50 times more effective than aniline—without the unpleasant smell of either. The only trouble with Ethyl was that it left a solid deposit in the engine, which eroded spark plugs and burned exhaust valves. More extensive tests proved that addition of a bromine compound or a bromine-plus-chlorine compound would correct this trouble.

Inherent in this solution was another difficult question. The reduction in fuel waste effected by the development of Ethyl had created a big new engineering problem of demand. The major available source of bromine in the '20s was the brine of salt wells, hardly adequate for the great demand which would be created by the marketing of no-knock high-test gasoline. Bromine was also present in seawater, but only in minute quantities—60 to 65 parts of bromine in a million parts of ocean water. The problem seemed unsolvable. Nevertheless, chemical engineers dug into it, and in 1933 Dow Chemical Company built a production plant at Wilmington, North Carolina, which used standard and well-known processes to recover pure bromine from seawater at the rate of 50,000 pounds a day.

Less knock with plump molecules

The high-test gasoline used today owes its effectiveness not only to no-knock additives but also to a series of innovations in petroleum refining—again pioneered by Kettering's researchers at General Motors. "Kettering," Boyd recalled, "said he did not believe that Nature could have had the automobile in mind when she made petroleum, any more than the hog intended his bristles for tooth-brushes. So he wanted to find out just what kinds of hydrocarbons are best in gasoline, and then if possible to discover ways of converting natural products into such materials." In effect, the engineers found out that gasoline is less likely to knock if it is made from short and plump oil molecules than if it consists of long and skinny molecules. The refining process that creates this more effective fuel, plus the supplementary no-knock effect of tetraethyl lead additive, have produced modern gasoline, two gallons of which can do as much work as three gallons of gasoline did 35 years ago.

The value of the economies achieved by these engineering feats can be appraised in several ways. In the crassest terms, American motorists save cash, $10.5 billion a year, simply because they need to buy fewer gallons of gasoline to cover a given distance. From another view, they economize on time to gain convenience and pleasure: high-test gasoline makes possible high-compression engines, and their power permits quick and comfortable travel over long distances. Today a 200-mile trip to visit grandmother is, for many a family, just a routine jaunt. But for human society as a whole, the true economy of these related developments lies in their preservation of the world's resources. Because high-test gasoline goes farther, it consumes less of the world's limited supply of oil.

Triumphs in penny-pinching

When Midgley and Boyd increased the efficiency of automobile engines, they were following directly in the footsteps of James Watt. For improved techniques of converting fuels into useful power are a major concern of engineers. Perhaps the most diligent in this penny-pinching pursuit are the engineers of the electric utilities. To them, a saving of a fraction of a cent is a grand victory.

Thomas Edison's first major power station, at Pearl Street in New York in 1882, used about 10 pounds of coal to make electricity that would operate a reading lamp for 10 hours. Now that same amount of electricity can be generated from one pound of coal. The great rise in efficiency and generating capacity is due partly to the development of the steam turbine, which began to replace the reciprocating engine in power plants around the turn of the century, and which—fueled by coal, oil, gas or uranium—today generates about 75 per cent of America's electricity. (The remaining 25 per cent comes mainly from water power.) But the key improvement was similar to the one made in auto engines: higher pressures and higher temperatures. The greater the pressure of the steam, and the greater the difference between its temperatures at inlet and outlet, the greater the power that can be extracted from it. Generations of engineers have, bit by bit, refined turbines to raise steam pressures and temperatures, which increased efficiency and power output. The biggest engines of a half century ago, those installed to generate electricity for New York's subway system, operated at temperatures of 370° F., pressures of 175 pounds per square inch and outputs of 7,500 horsepower. Today's turbines have more than a million horsepower, and use steam at 1,000° F. and 2,520 pounds per square inch.

The drive toward ever-higher temperatures and pressures as a means of gaining efficiency in the generation of electricity was abruptly—but temporarily—slowed down by the advent of nuclear fuel after World War II; extreme temperatures in atomic power plants cause complications that are only now being solved.

An atomic reactor is simply a furnace; it produces heat from the fission of uranium atoms. To perform any work, this heat has to be applied. Usually this is done by circulating water through the reactor core. This heated water becomes slightly radioactive, and the turbines that operate on steam derived directly from the reactor must be very carefully guarded against leaks. A more conservative scheme, first used in

Admiral Hyman G. Rickover's phenomenally successful submarine engines, was later adapted to civilian atomic power plants. In this method, the water in direct contact with the reactor is kept completely sealed in pipes and under such pressure that it never becomes steam. However, the heat of this radioactive water is applied to a completely separate source of nonradioactive water, which does boil into steam. It is this secondary steam that drives turbine generators and produces electricity.

Problems such as absolutely leakproofing pipes and turbines that also have to withstand atomic radiation have limited the temperatures which can be obtained from atomic furnaces. As a consequence, the pressures of the secondary steam driving the turbines are also limited. Recent improvements in materials and techniques have lessened these restrictions, but even with their continuing limitations, the economies offered by nuclear-fueled generators are stimulating the building of atomic power plants all over the world. One of the largest, being planned by Consolidated Edison for Indian Point, New York, will produce 837,000 kilowatts of electricity. Its reactor will consume a ton of enriched uranium every four years. In that time a conventional plant of the same capacity would have burned eight million tons of coal.

The efficiency of electric power plants, as they grow larger and more powerful, depends not only on getting more kilowatt-hours out of less fuel but also on getting the most use of the immensely expensive machinery, which continues to eat up dollars whether it is producing electric power or not. Even if a big generator is turning, it loses money if its load is far below its capacity. If a utility company hopes to earn a profit without charging its customers unreasonable rates, it should be producing and selling between 60 and 70 per cent of its generating capacity around the clock. Unfortunately, the demand for electricity falls off sharply in the late night and early morning hours.

Solving the slack period

Utility engineers have found an ingenious solution to the problem of the slack period. They include in the system a hydroelectric power plant, and use it for what is called "pumped storage." Electricity cannot be stored economically in large quantities in slack times for use during the rush hours, but water for generating electric power can. The pumped-storage plan calls for a waterside hydroelectric power plant with an elevated storage reservoir nearby. During quiet hours, when there is a surplus of power, engineers use this excess electricity to pump water up into the reservoir. The water pumps are driven by big motors and this machinery is reversible—during the busy hours when the system needs all the power it can generate, the water is released from storage, running back through the pumps, which now function as turbines, and turning the motors, which then work as generators.

One such pumped-storage plant was designed for an energy-producing efficiency of about 66 per cent; one and a half kilowatt-hours of electricity would be used to pump an amount of water which would return

INFLOW

STORAGE

OUTFLOW

HARNESSING THE TIDES is an effective way in which engineers utilize natural sources of power. The drawings above indicate how this is done with turbines at a dam that spans the mouth of France's Rance River, where tides from the English Channel rise and fall 40 feet and more. On an incoming tide, the blades of 24 turbines spin and generate power as water flows past them into the dam's reservoir. The water is then stored in the reservoir until ebb tide, when the turbines are reversed to generate more power as the water rushes seaward.

one kilowatt-hour in generated power. However, the cost of a kilowatt-hour used in the slack midnight period is much less than the value of a kilowatt-hour generated during the busy early evening, so the method makes good financial sense.

In another variation, the Connecticut Light and Power Company has a pumped-storage plant system between the Housatonic River and Candlewood Lake, which is geared for wet and dry seasons of the year instead of for day and night loads. When the river is high in the spring, water is stored in the lake for use in summer dry spells.

Free and limitless fuels

Pumped storage and improved turbines reduce the cost of the fuel consumed in producing electricity. With some other sources of energy, the saving can be immense, for these "fuels" are "free" and limitless. Water power, already widely exploited with dams, is one. The wind still turns mills to light some farms and pump their water. The free energy of the sun is also being captured for specialized uses. Now utility engineers are turning their attention to more exotic sources: the force of ocean tides and the energy of underground steam and hot water emerging from geysers and other natural vents. All of these sources are essentially inexhaustible and their use conserves the nonrenewable supplies of coal and oil. All are free—at least in one sense: the "fuel" itself costs nothing, but the plant for exploiting it may cost a great deal, and this weighs heavily in the engineer's balancing of economies.

The free energy of the tides has already been harnessed in France, where a dam containing 24 reversible turbine generators crosses the Rance River on the English Channel coast. The rise and fall of tides in the estuary carries millions of tons of water back and forth once every 12 hours. Since the turbines are reversible, they can be used to generate power during the time that the water is rushing in from the Channel and again when the water is released from the dam's reservoir.

While projects for generating electricity by harnessing the tides are fairly new, the free heat from sources inside the earth has been tapped usefully and economically for many years. In Iceland, an island which is actually the upper part of a mild-mannered volcano, the hot water from underground is gentle and pure enough to be piped directly to kitchen and bathroom faucets and outdoor swimming pools with no treatment except cooling and filtering to remove its slight amount of sediment.

In several other parts of the world, steam erupting from driven wells produces electricity commercially. The oldest of these geothermal plants, at Larderello in the Tuscany district of Italy, has been generating electricity since before World War I. Its turbogenerators now yield some two billion kilowatt-hours a year, enough to supply cities and to run part of Italy's railroad system. Two other plants, more recently placed in operation, are in New Zealand at Wairakei Valley and at The Geysers in California, a once popular hot springs resort in the mountains 92 miles north of San Francisco. Still other geothermal plants are being planned in Japan, Mexico, Central and South America, the Soviet Union and Iceland, which has been using its volcanic supplies only as a source of hot water.

The money-saving in fuel offered by a geothermal plant is often offset by the cost of installation, which may be complicated by the inaccessibility, pressure, quality or quantity of the steam. Power was first generated from Larderello's volcanic steam in 1894, when it was successfully used to boil a separate supply of nonvolcanic water: the pure steam then drove a nine-horsepower steam engine. Later several attempts were made to use volcanic steam directly to drive paddle wheels and a 40-horsepower steam engine coupled to a dynamo. Because the volcanic steam is heavily loaded with dissolved chemicals, including boric acid, hydrogen sulfide and ammonia, it quickly corroded every piece of machinery that it touched. For this reason, the Italian engineers went back to the original 1894 concept, using the heat of the volcanic steam but not its pressure. The same procedure was followed when the first modern steam turbogenerator was installed at Larderello in 1913, and indirect application of the steam's energy has been used ever since.

Profits from impurities

The complications caused by the corrosive effect of the varied and heavy chemical content of the volcanic steam turned out to be advantageous, however, because these impurities became highly profitable by-products. Along with its generation of electricity, Larderello does a big business in chemicals, extracting from its steam large quantities of carbon dioxide, boric acid, methane, ammonia, hydrogen and hydrogen sulfide (which can be converted into sulfuric acid). The steam also contains minute amounts (one part in 100,000) of helium, argon and xenon gases, carefully salvaged because of their high value. As a glowing tribute to waste-not engineering, Larderello is hard to beat.

Because the smaller and newer geothermal generating plants in New Zealand and California are not faced with Larderello's corrosion problem, they can utilize their steam directly. The New Zealand plant has its turbogenerators at the edge of the Waikato River nearly a mile from the volcanic steam wells, for a good engineering reason. Bringing the volcanic steam from the wells to the river is more economical than pumping cooling water from the river to the steam fields. In addition, the cool river water condenses exhaust steam at the outlets of the turbines. By condensing this exhaust steam in an enclosed chamber, a partial vacuum is created. The vacuum increases suction pressure at the inlets, thus intensifying the flow of piped volcanic steam to the turbines.

As compared with the Wairakei Valley plant's capacity of 192,000 kilowatts, the plant at The Geysers in California is small, producing 53,500 kilowatts—enough for a community of 60,000 people. The Geysers' steam contains only small amounts of dissolved chemicals and can therefore be fed to the generating plant directly. One problem arose with the charge of rock particles in the steam, but these are spun off in cen-

A PRIMITIVE VOLCANIC FURNACE, shown on the insignia of Italy's Larderello Company, was used to extract boric acid from volcanic water early in the 19th Century. Designed by Francesco de Larderel, the brick domes were built directly over or close to volcanic geysers that abound in a small area of Tuscany. Inside, the water was held in lead pans and evaporated by the heat of the steam, leaving the boric acid. Later, the company's engineers built the first successful volcanic power plant, using the steam to run a turbine.

trifugal cleaners. The plant is automatically controlled. If anything goes wrong, safety devices shut off part or all of the unit or the whole system, and an electronic warning summons the nearest technicians, 35 miles away at a centralized control station for the power grid.

Resources in sea and air

While "free" underground steam is becoming an increasingly important asset, engineers have long been making use of two of this planet's most readily available materials—seawater, which covers three quarters of the globe, and the atmosphere, which covers all of it.

Ordinary air and water are the sources of most of the world's ammonia, whose most important use is as an ingredient in making fertilizer to help grow food for our planet's teeming populations. Ammonia is made from nitrogen and hydrogen gases, both of which can be produced in several ways. Hydrogen gas can be obtained as a by-product of petroleum refining, by passing air and steam through coke, or by electrolysis of water. Nitrogen gas is also obtained by passing air and steam through coke, or by the distillation of liquid air. To combine the nitrogen and hydrogen into ammonia, the two gases are simply heated to 900° F., compressed up to 15,000 pounds per square inch and passed over a finely ground mixture of iron, aluminum, potassium and other metals. The metal powders stimulate the hydrogen to react with nitrogen gas to form ammonia, which is then processed into nitrate compounds, the basic materials of fertilizers and explosives. Before 1910, when Fritz Haber of Germany worked out this synthetic method, most nitrates came from natural beds of nitrate salts, located principally in Chile. During World War I, Germany's supplies of nitrates were cut off by naval blockade. Deprived of these necessities for military and agricultural production, Germany would have been unable to wage war if Karl Bosch, a brilliant chemical engineer, had not adapted the Haber process to mass production. Today most of the natural nitrate beds are depleted and the world's urgently needed nitrogen compounds are made from air and water by the Haber-Bosch method.

After the atmosphere the next handiest source of materials is the sea, and it is dipped into for a variety of minerals, even though they are thinly dispersed in the water. The bromine for no-knock gasoline comes from ocean water, and so does 90 per cent of America's magnesium, the lighter-than-aluminum metal essential for airplane parts but also used for cooking pots. The magnesium refining process, in particular, is a testimonial to the modern engineer's skill at getting the most from the least, for there is barely more than one part of magnesium in a thousand parts of ocean water. A magnesium griddle is made of about two pounds of metal. Although they required the processing of 250 gallons of water,

THE SOLVAY PROCESS was devised by Ernest Solvay in 1861 to synthesize soda ash, used in making glass, soap and other products. Because it requires only four materials—and reuses two of them—the process is regarded by engineers as a classic example of efficiency and conservation. In the first step, chilled brine is mixed with gaseous ammonia and then carbon dioxide in a carbonating tower to make sodium bicarbonate and ammonium chloride. When the bicarbonate is heated, the carbon dioxide is recovered, leaving the desired soda ash. Meanwhile, ammonia and calcium chloride are produced by adding slaked lime to the ammonium chloride. The ammonia is used to start the process again, while the calcium chloride, a dehydrating agent, is sold.

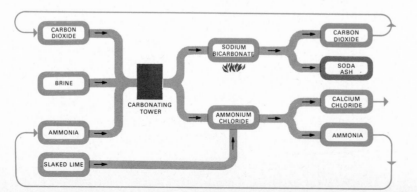

those two pounds of metal were sold by the refinery for only 60 cents.

Despite the brilliant advances of modern technology, one of the greatest achievements in waste-not-want-not engineering is more than a century old, the process for making soda ash from common salt. Soda ash is sodium carbonate—washing soda to housewives who once used it for softening laundry water. To industry, soda ash is one of the most basic of materials in the production of glass, paper, soap and textiles.

Because soda ash is so widely used in such great quantities, even a small saving in its cost is important. But the process devised in 1861 by 23-year-old Ernest Solvay is remarkable for more than its cash savings. It makes soda ash by several steps, and each of these steps requires a number of different materials, some of which are expensive. Only an infinitesimal amount of the expensive processing substances are consumed; they are almost totally recovered for reuse. Only the commonest substances are used up, and even they are converted into salable products.

The recoverable essentials

Solvay created his process while experimenting with the removal of ammonia and carbon dioxide gases from illuminating gas, which was produced at his family's plant near Brussels, Belgium. The gases were a costly nuisance, and Solvay found a way to convert this loss into substantial revenue. In a series of reactions, he combined the ammonia and carbon dioxide with salt water to get sodium bicarbonate and ammonium chloride. The bicarbonate, when heated, yielded the desired soda ash and also released the carbon dioxide gas to be used again. The ammonium chloride was treated with a slurry of lime to recover the ammonia for reuse; the residue was calcium chloride, a deicing and dehumidifying agent. In all these steps the only substances consumed were salt water, limestone and coke used for heating (the coke was a by-product of the family gas plant). The ammonia and carbon dioxide gases, essential to the working of the process, were consumed at one step, only to be regenerated and recovered at another. Since it takes one dollar's worth of ammonia to make one dollar's worth of soda ash, the whole scheme depends on strict adherence to absolute economy.

Even today, while soda-ash consumption multiplies, the Solvay process remains an engineer's ideal. The world's largest plant, near Syracuse, New York, differs from the original Belgian factory only in details of materials and design. Drawing limestone from quarries at nearby Jamesville and salt from the vast underground beds of the neighboring Tully Valley, the Syracuse installation produces 2,900 tons of 99.6 per cent pure soda ash a day. Its seven-story-high ammoniating towers, using the same costly gas over and over again, are the kind of monument an engineer would choose to mark his role as conserver of man's resources.

The Most
for the Least

Like a Yankee farmer, the engineer makes do. Husbanding materials and energy, he tries to get the most for the least. He conserves rare substances, such as the platinum catalysts needed for oil refining, by using them over and over again. He exploits the readiest sources, diligently squeezing from the atmosphere and oceans useful elements like nitrogen and magnesium.

This waste-not, want-not approach is close to the hearts of mining engineers, particularly in iron mines. So long as high-grade, easily mined hematite ore was available, the engineers concentrated on finding efficient ways to dig it out of the ground. In some mines, they left untouched the low-grade taconite ore nearby, since the extra effort of extracting it and refining it was not justified—at that time. But when the rich deposits were depleted, engineers were ready with ways of exploiting the lean. Methods had already been developed for breaking up the taconite—one of the hardest rocks known—and prying out its minute particles of usable iron. Once these techniques were put to use they proved so efficient that today they are used to process most of America's iron ore.

MINING WITH MUSCLE POWER

Sledges swinging, 19th Century miners drill a blasthole in the rich, ore-bearing rock ledge at an early Lake Superior iron mine. The primitive, hand-held drill cut into the rock at a rate of only five inches an hour. Later, to achieve mass-production mining, complex machinery and expensive engineering techniques were developed to wrestle other, more stubborn ore from the earth.

Early Mining:
The Easier Times

For more than half a century, America's greatest treasury of iron ore has been the Mesabi Range in Minnesota. Here rich deposits of high-grade hematite ore lay close to the surface, sometimes hidden only by a layer of pine needles. At first, miners with picks and shovels worked the prime deposits. Then came steam shovels, scooping out the earthy, rust-colored hematite like sugar from a bowl.

The first problem that faced the engineers was handling materials on a massive scale: how to move more ore, faster and faster, for less and less cost. Their solution was machinery. Railroad tracks were run into the mine pits, and early steam engines gave way to more efficient diesel units. Primitive drills for sinking blastholes—at first steel corkscrews battered home by sledgehammers—were replaced by machine rigs which pounded the bits like pile drivers. Cumbersome steam shovels, requiring expensive coal for fuel, evolved into powerful, electric-driven giants which tore out the ore at 16 tons a bite. In some places, factories were set up to wash out the sandy material found in the lower-grade hematite deposits—a procedure borrowed from copper and gold mining.

As output soared, Mesabi hematite grew into the bone and sinew of America's industrial strength. In 1942, the peak year, more than 70 million tons of ore left the Mesabi pits. As long as the rich hematite held out, the only problem facing the engineer remained how to get it out of the ground quickly and cheaply.

THE GREAT OPEN-PIT
In a typical open-pit operation near the turn of the century, an early steam shovel lifts a load of high-grade hematite ore from a Mesabi mine into waiting freight cars. Men with horses *(foreground)* plow away topsoil to uncover more ore. This pit, the Mahoning, eventually spread into the nearby Hull-Rust complex to form the world's largest open-pit iron mine. Over three miles long, it covers 1,500 acres and by 1949 had yielded 282,847,278 tons of iron ore.

Taconite: A First Experiment

Prospectors stubbed their toes on Mesabi taconite as early as 1870. This steel-gray stone, which was mingled with the mountain's richer hematite lodes, was considered too iron-poor to make good ore. But some engineers understood that when the high-grade hematite gave out, the only iron-bearing material they could work with would be varieties of taconite.

One such engineer was Edward W. Davis, an instructor at the University of Minnesota. In 1913, he began exploring ways to pry iron from taconite. Knowing that the iron-bearing part of taconite is magnetic, he developed a magnetic separator for dividing iron oxide from the impurities.

But even with Davis' separation method, the processed taconite was still too expensive to compete with high-grade ores. A taconite plant that Davis helped open in 1922 was a financial failure. But Davis kept looking for an economical taconite process ("I was a pest on the subject," he recalls), convinced that it would one day bring in valuable dividends.

TACONITE PIONEERS
Founding fathers of the world's first taconite mine sit for a portrait on a gas-driven railcar; this single railroad track was the only route to the mine. Edward W. Davis, at the far left, pioneered methods for upgrading the rock. Next to him are A. F. Benson, chief surveyor *(center)*, and Fred Jordan *(right foreground)*, who was in charge of operations at the pit. The mine was opened as a pilot project in 1916.

A LABORATORY SEPARATOR

In his laboratory at the University of Minnesota School of Mines, Edward W. Davis runs an ore sample through the magnetic-tube separator he developed for recovering iron oxide from powdered taconite. Later versions of Davis' separator are used today in laboratories and ore plants.

A PILOT RIG

The magnetic washer below is a full-sized version of the laboratory separator *(left)*. The ore, ground in the mill at the right of the picture, drops into the troughlike washer in foreground. Three powerful electromagnets under the trough collect the magnetite, and the water sluices away the silica. The device in the left background sorts out ore chunks according to size.

POUNDING THE ROCK
The first step in processing taconite to get at its iron-bearing magnetite is to break it into particles 17 ten-thousandths of an inch in diameter.

PULLING OUT THE IRON
Magnetite slivers cling to a magnet, showing how pulverized ore is separated from silica waste. Pure magnetite is about 65 per cent iron.

FORMING THE PELLETS
Powder-fine magnetite is built up into acorn-sized pellets for smelting in blast furnaces. All these steps are, of course, done by machinery.

Ore from a Tough Old Rock

Making use of low-grade, ore-bearing rock is a problem as tough as stone itself. Whether the task is iron mining or gold mining, engineers must first discover ways to dig out huge chunks of rock and to crush it fine enough to release the very small amount of ore it contains. Economical methods must then be found to separate usable ore from tons of unwanted waste. Finally, engineers may have to shape the separated ore into a form suitable for smelting into metal.

Taconite mining faces all these problems and some special difficulties of its own. Getting ore from taconite is, in fact, a bit like breaking out of prison. It means cracking open one of the toughest rocks known, for taconite confines minute grains of magnetite—magnetic iron oxide—in a silica binder. The rock's iron content (some 19 to 30 per cent) is less than half that needed for use in refineries.

Engineers came up with scientific blasting and crushing techniques to break up the taconite. They speeded up the job of sinking blastholes in the mine face with a drill that substitutes a rock-searing jet of flame for a steel drill bit. To crush this tough rock, the engineers lined a huge gyrating crusher *(far right)* with special abrasion-resistant alloys.

Then the experts began looking for ways of sorting out the crushed magnetite from the silica waste. They tested dozens of possible methods. In the end, a souped-up version of the magnetic separator developed years earlier by Edward W. Davis turned out to be the most economical device.

A BLOWTORCH FOR DRILLING

Like a science fiction disintegrator ray, a searing 4,300° F. jet flame melts a blasthole in a taconite mine. Steel drills can be uneconomically slow, biting only a foot an hour into the rock. But this drill can sink a shaft up to 10 inches in diameter at a fast rate of 40 feet an hour.

LITTLE ONES OUT OF BIG ONES

The world's largest rockcrusher is a 167-foot-deep gyratory pulverizer at the Reserve Mining Company's taconite mine in the Mesabi. In this sketch, a moving central cone is shown pounding the rock against the crusher's durable, alloy steel sides. Handling 60 tons of rock a minute, it can hammer boulders large as grand pianos into chunks the size of watermelons.

A PRODUCTION-LINE DUMPER
Reserve Mining's unique rotary car unloader, which dumps standard-gage railroad cars without uncoupling, sends crushed taconite cascading onto a conveyor belt. Special swivel couplings allow the dumper to tip up cars two at a time while they are still attached to the train.

A HALF MILE OF GRINDERS
Ranks of grinding mills, extending the 2,640-foot length of Reserve's concentrating plant, spin mixtures of crushed taconite and water. Rock particles tear into each other and into tough steel balls or rods as the grinders turn—pummeling the ore to a face-powder fineness.

Making a Better Grade

"Beneficiation" is the engineers' five-dollar word for the process involved in getting pay dirt out of dirt-poor material. The price of beneficiating is measured in millions of dollars—in plant machinery and complex techniques. But at the $350-million Reserve Mining Company plant in Minnesota, engineers have developed a system for turning out more than 10 million tons of usable iron ore a year. In the long run, such volume makes the process extremely economical.

The beneficiating procedure begins as the ore is crushed and ground fine enough to separate particles of iron ore from sandy wastes. A series of 66 grinding machines reduce the chunks of ore to fragments and then to motes. Finally, a battery of 44 water separators and 352 magnetic finishers shuffles out the magnetite.

With some iron ores, such as low-grade hematite, engineers can use simpler practices. Sometimes they sluice away impurities with water, just as prospectors pan gold. Occasionally, iron oxide is collected with chemicals in giant flotation tanks. But no matter how it is done, beneficiation lets miners exploit ore so inferior it would otherwise be wasted.

A BATTERY OF SEPARATORS

Minuscule grains of pulverized ore from the grinders, suspended in water, are fed into rows of separators to remove the sandy impurities. In the vats at right, part of the sandlike silica is floated away. Magnetic separators *(center)* segregate magnetite ore, which is then rolled into pellets. Ore is upgraded to between 60 and 65 per cent iron in order to be acceptable.

Revolution for the Blast Furnaces

After crude rock has been converted by beneficiation to useful ore concentrate, one problem remains: how to put it in a form that can be shipped and smelted. Magnetite is so dusty fine that if it were processed in its original form, much of it would blow away in shipping and the rest would be vomited out like smoke from the stacks of the blast furnaces. The engineers' solution was to roll the magnetite into pellets—tough, porous marbles of concentrated ore. Muddy ore from the magnetic separators is dropped into tilted revolving drums. As it tumbles down the sides of the drums, like snowballs rolling down a hill, it gathers into pellets. These are baked hard for shipping.

The development of these pellets has revolutionized the iron industry. Twice as efficient as older materials for blast furnaces, pellets today are widely used in foreign countries as well as throughout the United States.

LIKE PEAS FROM A POD
Taconite pioneer Davis fills his hand with new-made pellets from a revolving drum. A scraper *(top)* prevents a build-up of concentrate on the drum's sides and ensures uniform pellet size. Two decades of research went into making the pellets, first available commercially in 1955.

CARLOADS OF CONCENTRATE
Baked hard in a conveyor-belt furnace, steaming pellets drop from a chute into moving rail-cars. Pellets must be stockpiled during the long sub-zero Minnesota winter when ice floes clog the usual freighter routes across Lake Superior to blast furnaces in Illinois, Indiana and Ohio.

7

The Human Factor

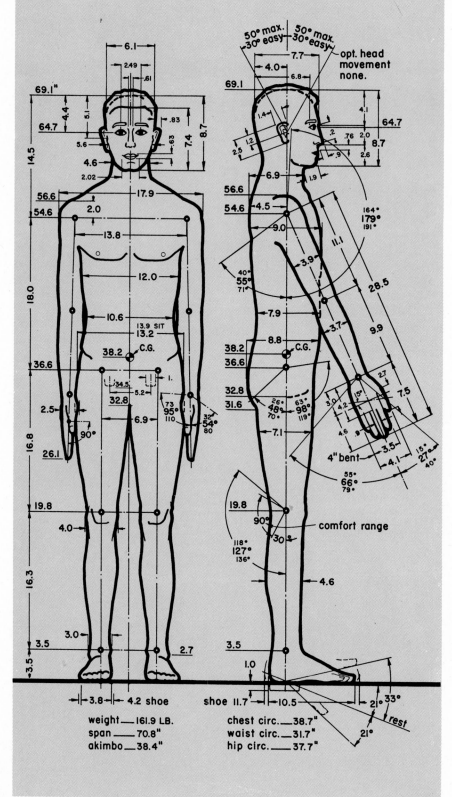

The average male, a composite drawn up from hundreds of statistics, serves as a model for human-factors engineers, who fit machines to men by designing products—from telephone dials to jet-plane cockpits—tailored for efficient human use.

MRS. ROSE COHEN is an attractive, dark-haired Brooklyn widow whose busy life includes housekeeping, work at home as a dressmaker, and frequent visits with her daughter and two grandchildren. The description may make Mrs. Cohen sound like hundreds of thousands of American women. But in one respect, she is most unusual. She is alive to enjoy her routine only because a tiny, battery-powered device known as a pacemaker has been implanted in the skin beneath her ribs. Wires carry the signals generated by the pacemaker into her heart to keep it beating steadily. Without this man-made rhythm-keeper, Mrs. Cohen's heart would soon falter and she would almost certainly die. She owes her life to a new breed of engineers: the bioengineers, who focus on the engineering problems and possibilities of living things. These engineers are still a small group, but the advances they have helped to bring about have already had an important impact on the lives of ordinary men and women. And they promise to have even more significant effects in the future.

The achievements of the bioengineer touch many areas of modern society, but most bioengineers specialize in one of three fields: medical engineering, human-factors engineering or bionics engineering. Man-made devices to prolong human life—the pacemaker is only one—are the work of one of these subgroups, the medical engineers. New machines and engineering systems, better suited to their purposes because they were designed with human needs and limitations in mind, are the specialty of another, the human-factors engineers. And the third subdivision includes the bionics engineers, who have set out to duplicate the feats of the greatest engineer of them all, nature itself.

The bionics engineer tries to translate into man-made systems the most valuable characteristics of various forms of animal life. This is an old idea. Greek mythology tells of Icarus, who tried to fly on wings copied from the birds, only to perish when he flew too near the sun and his waxen wings melted in the blazing heat. And in the early 16th Century, that extraordinarily fertile genius, Leonardo da Vinci, laid out detailed plans for a flying machine also based on the structure of the bird's wings.

But, as any modern engineer could have predicted, neither idea could possibly have worked. Direct copying of nature is rarely successful, and this is what these early dreamers had proposed: the creation of exact replicas of a bird's flight structures. Orville and Wilbur Wright succeeded in making the first airplane because they were, in a sense, expert bionics engineers. They based their design on the processes that make flight possible. They thought primarily in terms of function, rather than structure, and it was function they sought to imitate in their machine.

Any number of lowly creatures have abilities bionics engineers would like to duplicate. Certain fish are so sensitive to the minute electrical changes in the water around them that they will respond if a visitor rubs a comb to charge it with electricity and then waves it in front of their tank. Only such highly refined voltmeters as electrometers are comparably sensitive. The porpoise emits a series of high-pitched squeaks as it swims; it interprets the echoes that bounce back with such uncanny accuracy that it can detect the presence and location of underwater obstacles long before they appear in view, and can even distinguish between one kind of food fish and another. Sonar, the man-made counterpart of this echolocating system, permits ships and submarines to protect themselves against underwater dangers. But sonar compares to the porpoise's apparatus as a toy telescope does to the huge instrument at Mount Palomar.

One creature that has already served as a model for bionics engineers —and with significant results—is the beetle. Its unusual eyes respond with extraordinary speed and accuracy to moving shadows. This visual ability inspired the development of a new and extremely efficient system of aerial photography.

A camera based on an insect's eye

The original investigations that led to the development of the new camera system were conducted by a team of young Germans, Werner Reichardt, an engineer, and Bernhard Hasselstein, a biologist. Through a series of ingenious experiments, Hasselstein and Reichardt discovered a relationship between the beetle's multifaceted eye structure and the way the creature behaves. They studied the movements of a beetle when the ground on which it stood was illuminated with a moving pattern of light and shade, and found that its choice of path and the speed with which it moved depended on the light pattern at that moment. Apparently, the beetle perceives shadows as they pass from one eye facet to another. Its behavior seems to be affected by the patterns of brightness and darkness that fall successively on these facets, and these patterns may indicate the location and speed of approach of potential danger.

In the United States, engineers specializing in the design of equipment for aerial reconnaissance quickly recognized the utility of this principle. These men were troubled by a problem that all aerial reconnaissance photographers face. Because the aerial camera moves at the same extremely high speed as the airplane in which it is carried, the photographer cannot take clear pictures of objects on the ground unless his film moves, too. But the film must move at precisely the correct rate; too fast or too slow, and the picture will be blurred. Imitating the principle of the beetle's eye provided a way of determining the correct film speed. Two photocells—each analogous to one facet of the eye—are placed in the airplane, several feet apart. As the airplane flies, the light changes produced by the appearance of an object on the ground are registered on each of the photocells in turn. Correlating information on the time lapse between the first and second registrations with information on the speed and altitude of the aircraft, the photographer can easily determine how fast he must move his film to guarantee a clear picture.

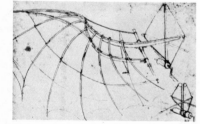

A WING FOR FLIGHT, powered by human muscles, was sketched by Leonardo da Vinci at the end of the 15th Century after he had meticulously studied and recorded the structural details of birds' wings. Leonardo left instructions for making his wings from fir bows, fustian and feathers, but his "flying machine" was never built—nor would this early attempt at bionics have succeeded. Leonardo copied his biological model too slavishly, without considering other problems, such as the fact that a bird's flying muscles, in proportion to its weight, are about 20 times the size of a man's equivalent pectoral muscles.

While bionics engineers attempt to translate natural abilities into engineering systems, their brother specialists—human-factors engineers —try to make sure that the system will indeed suit human requirements. Their work, which often demands collaboration with psychologists, was given impetus by World War II, when it became painfully obvious that military success depended on an effective match between the machines of war—from airplanes to small arms—and the capacities and limitations of the men who used them. The mere recognition of this fact led to developments that, while seemingly simple or even obvious, had far-reaching effects.

Navy pilots, for example, flew a number of different kinds of planes, each differing in many characteristics. In a long-range bomber, a fuel supply of 500 gallons might be dangerously low, whereas in a single-engine fighter plane, this same amount would be sufficient for an entire mission. Since the fuel gauges in each plane indicated the fuel supply in gallons, pilots often became confused when they switched from one plane to another. In some cases, they thought they were in danger when in fact they were safe. In others, they failed to recognize that their tanks were indeed running dry, and they crashed. Human-factors engineers solved the problem—and in the simplest possible way: they changed the markings on the fuel gauges—and other instruments like them—from numbers to symbols. Instead of indicating the number of gallons of fuel in the tank, the symbols indicated the relative level: "full," "half full," "empty." This system is now in use in all aircraft and, as every driver knows, in every automobile.

Designing for safety

Similarly, human-factors engineers made an elementary but lifesaving alteration in the design of the knobs controlling the wing flaps, wheels and engine power on aircraft. Originally, all three knobs, which may be located next to one another in the cockpit, were identical in design and shape. In a tense situation, a pilot sometimes pulled the wrong knob. The result might be embarrassing: speeding along the ground after a landing, he might reach to raise the flaps but instead pull the wheel-retracting control and drop the plane on its belly. Or the mistake could be fatal: more than one pilot was killed during takeoff when, having achieved flying speed, he meant to retract the wheels but instead closed the throttle, which nosed the plane right into the ground. Reshaping the knobs into forms that represented the function they performed—a small wheel as the wheel control, for instance—enabled the pilot to use his sense of touch to tell him that he was using the proper control.

With the end of the war, human-factors engineers began to expand their area of concern to deal with much more complex and subtle prob-

AN AVIATION PIONEER, Otto Lilienthal made some 2,000 flights in gliders like the one below before he was killed in a crash in 1896. Like Leonardo, he copied the wings of birds in his designs. Modern bionics engineers, however, copy only the broad principles of an animal function, freely changing structural details to meet specific problems with the materials they have to work with.

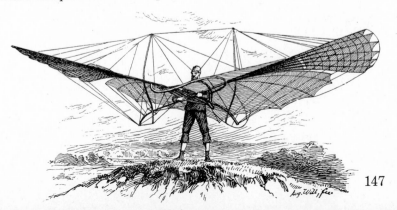

147

lems. A study by Ezra S. Krendel of the Franklin Institute in Philadelphia made it possible to express in mathematical terms one important aspect of the man-machine relationship—man's ability to control and guide machines. This factor could then be included in the engineering design of airplanes. Krendel and his associates constructed a simplified model of an airplane steering apparatus—a bucket seat and a control stick. In front of the seat they placed a cathode-ray oscilloscope that represented steering requirements by means of a randomly moving dot on its screen. The pilot's steering skill was gauged by asking him to manipulate the control in such a fashion as to keep the dot always in the center of the screen. By testing the reactions of a large number of pilots under many different sets of circumstances and measuring the speed and efficiency of their responses, Krendel was able to develop a mathematical formula which described the pilot's ability to coordinate hand and eye. With this formula aeronautical engineers could take the human factor into account and thus increase the plane's efficiency and margin of safety. Similar calculations for other machines that must be steered—from automobiles to aircraft—are now routine aspects of the design process.

All of the accomplishments of human-factors engineering have a very direct effect on people. But when the effect is primarily one of convenience rather than safety, it is not always obvious. Experience and habit inure us to many minor hardships. The design of the typewriter keyboard, for example, made considerable engineering sense when the machine was first invented, in the late 19th Century. Since the typebars on the machine were heavy and jammed easily, the inventor, Christopher Latham Sholes, deliberately arranged the keyboard to keep a wide distance between the letters most frequently joined in words. With the development of the touch system, however, the human-factors weaknesses in his design became apparent. Because a touch typist uses all 10 fingers, her weaker left hand must then do far more work than the stronger right. Moreover, the weakest finger of all—the little finger of the left hand—must hit two of the most frequently used keys: the "a" and the capital-letter shift. Yet efforts to change the keyboard, to bring it into closer conformity with the structure of the English language and the human hand, have never been successful.

The obstacle of habit

One new arrangement, developed by August Dvorak of Washington State University, was tested by a group of federal employees in early 1956; had the test succeeded, the government planned to convert all its machines to the Dvorak keyboard. But the idea was abandoned after only four months. The typists found it so difficult to unlearn their old habit patterns that they simply could not make the adjustment. Fortunately, engineering has found another solution to the typists' problem of finger and hand fatigue: an electric typewriter is far easier and less tiring to operate than is a manual machine.

The story of the typewriter keyboard throws into sharp relief one of

ZEBRA-STRIPING A WOMAN was part of a photographic technique devised by human-factors engineer Jiro Kohara to check the relationship of body contours to bone structure. By using a special light filter, he was able to project vertical stripes on models in various positions. The resulting contour-tracing patterns, matched with anthropological data on bone structure, provided new guidelines for the design of chairs and other furniture.

the major problems with which the human-factors engineer must always deal: the strength of human habit patterns.

In 1949, for example, telephone company engineers developed a new and somewhat larger housing for the telephone, which made the instrument steadier, and therefore easier to use. As the human-factors engineers recognized, this new housing also made it possible to move the letters and digits on the dial from their original positions underneath the finger holes to places outside them, on the perimeter of the dial. On first thought it would have seemed that this simple innovation, which keeps the digits always in sight, even during dialing, would reduce the chance of getting a wrong number. But when the new arrangement was tested, it was found that dialing errors had actually increased. The digits had served as guides when they were underneath the finger holes. But when they were moved to the perimeter of the dial, the telephone user lost his targets. It was only when dots were placed inside the finger holes, as substitute aiming points, that the number of dialing errors dropped. In a short time the advantages of the new arrangement became apparent.

For enterprises like the telephone company, a human-factors engineering staff is virtually a necessity. Any change that is made—whether in the design of a telephone set or the organization of a service—has a very direct effect on millions of people, not only telephone company employees but telephone users as well. Unless these effects are taken into consideration, there can be no assurance that the change will meet with success.

Phoning with a computer's help

Human-factors studies are therefore part of the advance planning for every innovation the Bell System makes. In the next several years, for example, the information service may be taken over by a computer. When a telephone user calls Information for a number, the operator will no longer have to hunt through a directory to find it—as she does now—but will punch a few keys on a typewriterlike device, instructing the computer to search its memory files for the desired information.

When the information computer was first being planned, a human-factors engineering team, under the direction of the late Richard L. Deininger, a chemical engineer with a Ph.D. in experimental psychology, determined the extent to which the new system would be helpful—to the telephone company, to the information operator and to the customer. The engineers also proposed the memory system the computer should utilize and designed the language in which the information operator could speak—as it were—to the computer.

Investigating the potential advantages of a computer system, Deininger and his associates discovered that there are some circumstances under which even a computer would be hard put to improve on the present system. When the customer has precise information to offer, the operator can answer his request almost immediately: in calls for well-known businesses, the operator generally begins to quote the number 10 sec-

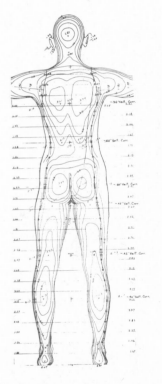

A HUMAN-CONTOUR MAP—similar to the type used by geologists to illustrate the topography of the earth's surface—is another of the new ways by which human-factors engineers can make detailed studies of the human figure. This technique, the most precise yet devised for measuring body surface area, not only helps in designing items which must be precisely sized, but is also being used in U.S. Air Force studies of radiation exposure.

onds after the customer starts to speak. But requests like "Can you give me the number of the gift store on Main Street?" or "Do you have the number for a Doctor Jones on Seventy-something Street?"—which all of us make from time to time—are far more difficult. Although answers can eventually be supplied if the customer is able to pin down things a little more exactly—by giving the name of another store nearby or by giving Dr. Jones's first name or full address—this takes considerable time. The information operator's directories, while more up-to-date and more carefully cross-indexed than those in general use, are still not sufficiently detailed to permit her to find the information without specific details.

If the information service were computerized, however, a far more complex cross-indexing system could be established, particularly for large metropolitan areas. The question about Dr. Jones—difficult or impossible to answer under the present system—could be answered easily by a computer designed to search all the city's listings for doctors, for names beginning with the letters JON, and for streets beginning with the number seven. What is more, the operator could suggest the listings that might give the reply in far less time and with far less effort than it now takes her to prod the customer for more information.

In establishing categories for the computer's memory, Deininger and his team focused their attention on the telephone user. They analyzed the kinds of facts that customers generally offer when they call, and thus were able to determine the general headings the memory system should contain. In designing the computer language, they focused their attention on the information operator. They tested the relative speed and accuracy with which she could type various kinds of proposed codes, and chose the most efficient one.

Engineering to prolong life

With automation of the telephone information service, the Bell System is attempting to link human thought processes directly to an engineering system. This bridge between the brain and the machine is the most delicate task that human-factors engineers face in tailoring their designs to suit people. But the third subgroup of bioengineers is attempting and succeeding in an even more intimate connection to the human body. They are medical engineers, and they are building machines—like Rose Cohen's pacemaker—that keep people alive and well. Such engineers helped develop the artificial kidney, a filtering system that, connected directly to the bloodstream of a patient whose own kidneys no longer function, purifies his blood and thus saves him from certain death. Similarly, engineers played a major part in the development of the heart-lung machine, which can take over the job of circulating the blood while a surgeon operates on the heart.

At the frontier of medical engineering is the work now being done in designing artificial organs—man-made devices that can be implanted in the body to replace parts of the system that are no longer in good working order. And some of the most important of these advances are being

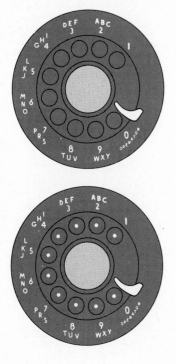

A TELEPHONE DIAL illustrates the seemingly minor details that human-factors engineers must consider in designing a product for efficient human use. In 1947 researchers at Bell Laboratories suggested that the dial then in use *(above)* be changed so that the average person could see the numbers from a wider angle. Engineers then designed a dial with the numbers outside the finger holes *(below)*. But when the dial was tested, the black holes proved difficult to distinguish and caused mistakes. A target dot was then added under each hole *(bottom)* and this dial, now in use, has greatly improved dialing ease and accuracy.

made in designing replacement parts for the most vital of all human organs—the heart.

The first of these devices to be widely used was the artificial heart valve, which prevents heart failure induced by leakage between the chambers of the heart. One particular type of valve—a marble-sized plastic ball encased in a miniature steel cage—already pops up and down inside the hearts of close to 100,000 Americans. It was designed by M. Lowell Edwards, a Portland, Oregon, engineer. Work on the project began in 1957, when Edwards, then recently retired from an extraordinarily creative engineering career—he holds 63 patents in the fields of aircraft, pulp and paper—became acquainted with Albert Starr of the University of Oregon and discovered how urgent was the need for an artificial device to be used as a heart valve. Natural valves are sometimes incorrectly shaped or damaged by disease; because they do not open or close properly, blood leaks between the chambers of the heart. Although several mechanical valves had already been designed and tried, none were effective.

Edwards' valve took nearly three years to perfect. But the time and effort were worthwhile. The valve consists of a ball of heat-cured silicone rubber, about three quarters of an inch in diameter, enclosed in a one-and-a-half-inch-high stainless steel cage. In September 1960 it was implanted in the heart of a 52-year-old Oregon man to repair damage resulting from rheumatic fever. He survived for almost 10 years, holding down a full-time job. Since 1967, valves covered with polyethylene cloth have been increasingly used, allowing complete healing as the cloth becomes lined with living tissue; the improved valve has upped the survival rate to 95 per cent. As Starr puts it: "The valve needed a surgeon to see how it might work, and an engineer to see how it could be made."

Equally dramatic is the effect of the pacemaker, Mrs. Cohen's electronic lifeline. This tiny machine takes over the small patch of tissue in the heart that normally beats time for the heart muscle. Like the coxswain of a racing shell calling the strokes for his oarsmen, this rhythm-keeper signals the muscle when to squeeze and when to relax. If the coxswain fails to control his crew, a race is lost. But if the heart's rhythm-keeper falters, as it does in Stokes-Adams disease, the results may be disastrous. Heart output weakens or even stops.

Electronic regulation of the heart

The man-made pacemaker works like the natural time-keeping tissue, signaling the heart muscles with rhythmic impulses of electricity. It had its beginnings in 1952, when Paul Zoll, of Beth Israel Hospital in Boston, conceived the notion of sending a pulse of energy to the heart through electrodes attached outside the chest wall. But so great an amount of energy was required to produce the necessary stimulation that the patients who used the earliest devices—which Zoll developed in cooperation with engineers at the Electrodyne Company—suffered severe burns on their skin and cramplike contractions of their chest muscles. In the next few years, advances in surgery and electronics made it possible to produce externally worn pacemakers whose electrodes could be led through the chest wall and attached directly to the heart. But these devices were bulky and uncomfortable to wear, and the patients often suffered infections at the point where the wire entered the chest.

At last, in 1960, two totally independent teams of investigators—Wilson Greatbatch, an electronics engineer, and William M. Chardack of the Veterans Administration Hospital in Buffalo, New York; and Adrian Kantrowitz of Brooklyn's Maimonides Hospital, who worked with engineers at General Electric Company—developed an internally worn pacemaker similar to the one that is in use today. Guided by their experience in building extremely tiny pulse generators for spacecraft, the engineers were able to create a signal generator small enough to be implanted within the body and yet powerful enough to supply a sufficient stimulus to the heart. But the wiring in these first models was inadequate; wiring fine enough to be used in such a small instrument was also so delicate that it broke easily. In the three years after her first operation, Mrs. Cohen had to have her pacemaker replaced three times because the wires broke and the machine stopped functioning.

In 1965, however, a team of engineers at General Electric's plant in Milwaukee, Wisconsin, redesigned the pacemaker's wiring system. Two mechanical engineers—David Fischer and Hugh Forman—and two electrical engineers—Wendell Pyle and David Bowers—developed a pacemaker based on an entirely new wire, called the helicable, which consists of 49 strands of stainless steel and silver wire, coiled together and then wound tightly into a spring. The total diameter of the spring is .0018 inch—only half as wide across as a strand of human hair.

The two-speed pacemaker

General Electric's engineers have also made other advances in the pacemaker. A two-speed device makes it possible to speed up or slow down the heart rate simply by passing a magnet over the portion of the chest beneath which the signal generator is implanted. In this way a person can increase his heart rate when he has to climb stairs or slow it down when he wants to take a nap. Even newer pacemakers, called "demand" units, have sensors that respond only when the heart beats abnormally and activate the unit to correct the condition.

The most exciting project, however, is the development of the completely artificial heart. Some of medicine's most prominent men have been instrumental in this work. Willem Kolff, who pioneered the artificial kidney machine, has headed artificial-heart teams at Cleveland Clinic, Cleveland, Ohio, and at the University of Utah. The famous heart

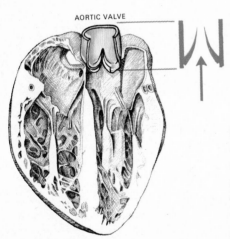

AORTIC VALVE

MAN-MADE HEART VALVES *(below)*, developed by teams of doctors and engineers, have made it possible to replace a natural heart valve, like the aortic valve shown above, when it becomes damaged by disease. Each version of the artificial valves was adapted from familiar types long utilized by mechanical engineers for household fixtures like furnace dampers and water closets. Each allows blood to flow out through an artery when the heart contracts, then seals off the opening until the next contraction to prevent backflow.

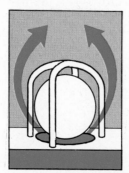

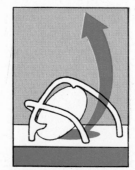

BALL-IN-CAGE VALVE   PIVOTING DISK VALVE   BUTTERFLY VALVE

surgeon Michael de Bakey, who developed the technique of replacing worn arteries with sections of Dacron tube, leads a group at Baylor College of Medicine in Houston, Texas. And Tetsuzo Akutsu, formerly of Maimonides Medical Center in Brooklyn, New York, is pursuing his life's work on the artificial heart at the University of Mississippi.

The basic design for a totally artificial heart, developed by Akutsu, closely resembles that of a natural heart. It has an inner flexible pumping chamber made of silicone rubber and an outer rigid housing of fiberglass resin, covered with silicone rubber. It is driven by a jet of compressed air introduced between these layers to squeeze blood out of the inner chamber just as a muscular contraction does in the normal heart. The flow of air is regulated very precisely by electronic controls. With the help of such electronic devices the artificial heart can be made to function just like a natural heart.

And yet, some very basic problems remain unsolved. One is how to provide the energy that will keep the artificial heart going. The patient, obviously, cannot be plugged into a wall outlet 24 hours a day, nor can he comfortably carry around a six- or seven-pound battery required to supply the necessary 30 watts of power. Ideally, the energy source would be implanted in the body together with the artificial heart and for this reason would have to be very compact. The best promise for developing such an internal power plant lies in the use of Plutonium 238 as nuclear fuel, providing it is safe to man.

Seeking material for an artificial heart

Another, and perhaps more serious, obstacle is the fact that a perfect material for the artificial heart has not yet been found. The substance must be strong and durable, impervious to attack by body fluids and tissues and harmless to the patient's body. Most of all, it must be compatible with human blood so that it does not cause clots.

To date, the material that meets these specifications best is silicone rubber. But it still has serious defects. For one, it tears easily and must be reinforced with some stronger material, like Dacron mesh. Also, it has sometimes caused small blood clots in experimental animals. Most researchers, including Akutsu himself, agree that the solution to the problem of developing an artificial heart may finally depend on the polymer chemist and the chemical engineer. If they can design a giant molecule with the necessary properties, they will have gone a long way in determining whether or not the human heart can ever be totally replaced.

Akutsu is a cautious man. "I have no idea," he says, "when our work will finally be successful. Whenever someone asks me, I always say, 'Ten years.' If physicians and engineers, both, are successful, that prophecy may come true."

Building Machines
to Fit Men

Every time a man dials a telephone, drives a car or studies a radarscope he has joined his sensing, decision-making and muscular powers to an engineering system. If he pushes the wrong button—or panics when he must watch too many dials, or grows uncomfortable in his chair—the system is not working properly. The penalty of error can be disaster: in a 22-month period during World War II, 457 U.S. Air Force accidents were caused by pilots who confused landing gear and flap controls. The job of designing controls that could be more easily recognized fell to human-factors engineers—experts on the way men operate machines.

These engineers deal with such varied problems as finding the ideal size for finger holes in a telephone dial, determining the proper firmness of a bed (right), and designing highway signs that are legible to a driver traveling at 60 miles an hour. Wherever a man is in contact with a machine—guiding it, sitting on it, watching it or wearing it—the knowledge of the human-factors engineer becomes vital, for the machine will be successful only if its design takes into account the skills and shortcomings of its operator.

A MAP FOR A GOOD NIGHT'S REST
To find out why soft beds interfere with sleep, human-factors engineers made charts (right) of the distribution of body pressure on a hard and a soft mattress. The chart of the harder mattress, on the left, shows concentration of support on relatively insensitive areas of the body; the soft mattress, however, disturbs a sleeper because it applies pressure to sensitive as well as dull areas.

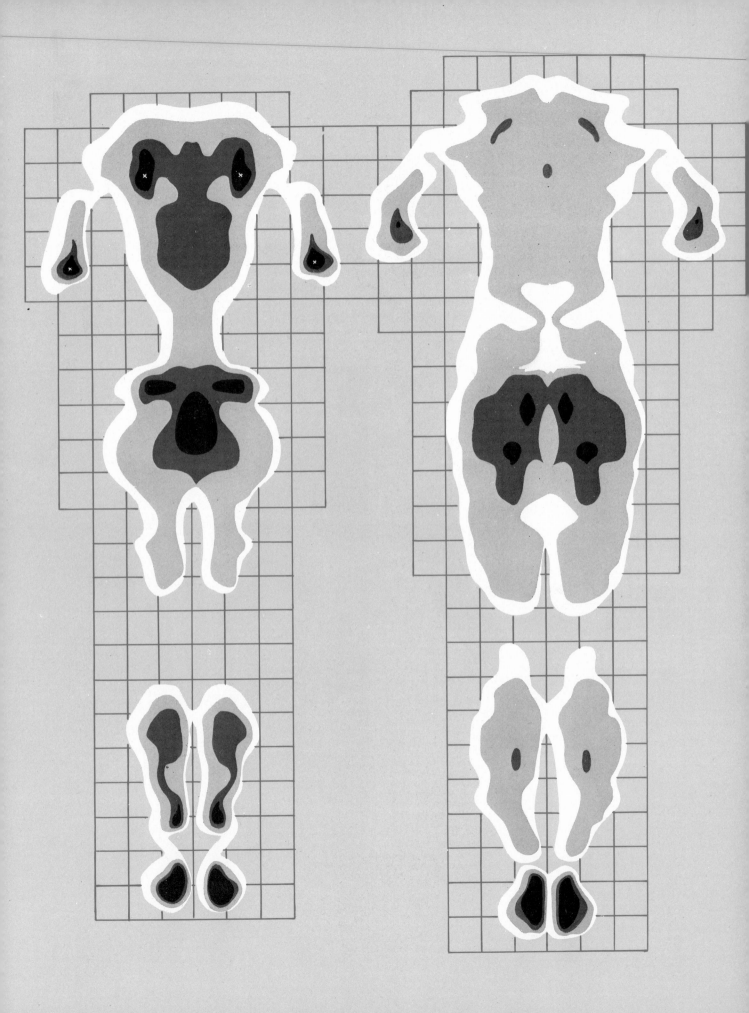

Cautious Changes
for the Telephone

Almost 300 million times a day, Americans use their telephones. Unlike most machines, this indispensable instrument must be easily operable by men, women and children alike, so every change of design, no matter how small, is preceded by elaborate engineering tests. More human-factors engineering has gone into the telephone than into any other non-military device. For example, when engineers were working on a new telephone handset in 1937 they measured 2,000 male and female heads before arriving at a diagram, similar to the one below, showing the average-sized human head. Later the handset was given slightly greater curvature and shortened by about one half inch to bring the mouthpiece closer to the average caller's mouth.

The human-factors engineers who first tackled the problem of designing a telephone with the dial in the handset *(opposite, below)* faced a baffling problem. For greatest convenience, dial finger holes must be at least a half inch across, but a dial with these specifications made the handset too bulky to hold. They tried replacing finger holes with spokes, but found that fingers slipped off and wrong numbers were dialed. Finally they found a way to reduce the diameter of the dial by using a movable finger-stop and eliminating the space between 1 and 0. The result: a telephone that is designed to fit the fingers, hands and heads of millions of callers.

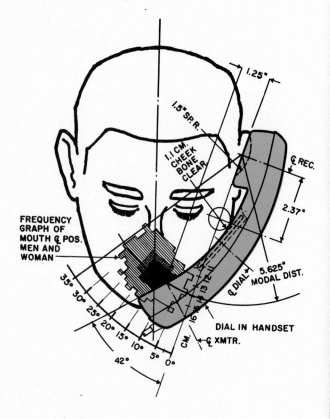

AN AVERAGE CALLER'S HEAD
In determining the best shape for handsets, human-factors engineers used an anthropometric chart like the one above—a composite of thousands of head measurements. Each of the shades near the mouthpiece represents the ear-to-mouth distance of 20 per cent of the population.

COMBINING FORM AND FUNCTION
Henry Dreyfuss, one of the leading industrial design consultants in the U.S., has advised the Bell Laboratories on all new telephone designs since 1930, including the dial-in-handset model at right. Dreyfuss has helped design other machines that range from sewing machines to tractors.

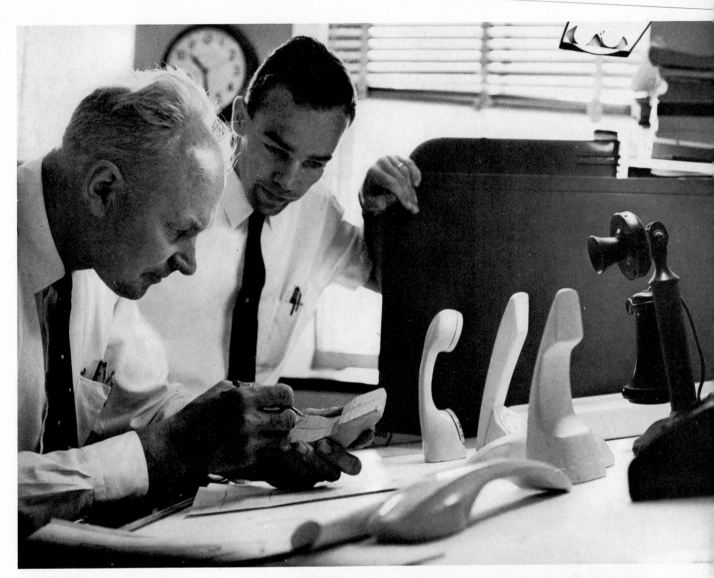

PHONES WITH A BUILT-IN BASE

Many variations on the theme of a dial-in-handset telephone, several of which are shown here, were examined by Bell Laboratories engineers to determine whether the necessary electronic components could be fitted into their bases. The technically acceptable versions were then tested for consumer preference by home-use trials throughout the United States.

EVOLUTION OF A DESIGN

Inspired by the simplicity of the lineman's test set—the model at left—Bell Laboratories engineers began looking for a practical dial-in-handset telephone in 1958. The dial of their final model is almost three eighths of an inch smaller in diameter than the dial of a preliminary model *(center)*, although the finger holes are exactly the same size. The bell is in a separate cradle.

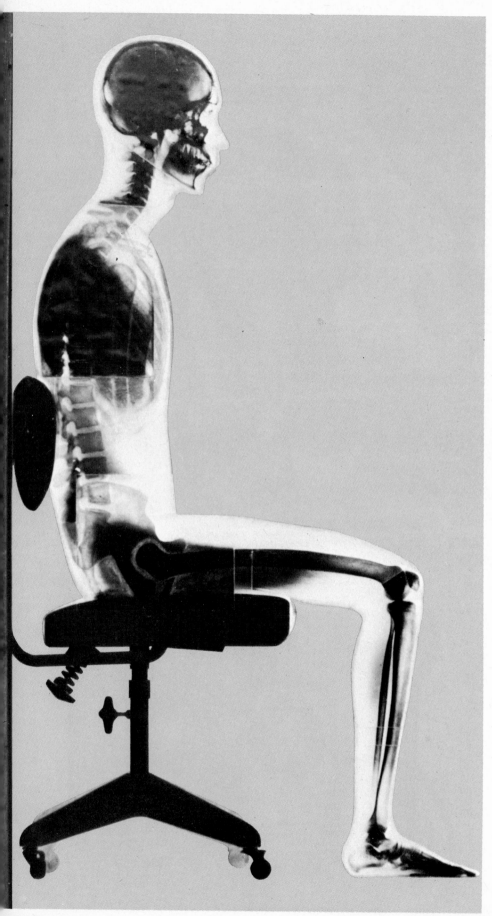

Relating Chairs to Bodily Mechanics

Sitting in a chair is not a universally adopted position of rest. Some peoples of the world stand on one leg; others kneel, squat or sit cross-legged on the ground. But in Westernized civilizations, the chair is man's answer to the need for nonsleeping rest. Often the chair must support the body of a secretary or businessman for eight hours a day. Jiro Kohara, at the Chiba University in Japan, has systematically examined how chairs affect the body. His studies include X-ray photographs of skeletal positions, chemical tests of the pressure distribution on a seat cushion, films of body movements in a chair over long periods of time and electrical measurements of muscle fatigue.

If the seat of a chair is too high or too long, it may interfere with circulation by squeezing the blood vessels of the thighs, where they are close to the skin. If the back of a chair does not support the spine between the second and fourth lumbar vertebrae, abdominal and back muscles have to hold part of the body weight—and the result is discomfort and weariness. Soft cushions for chair seats are perhaps the worst offenders of all. Kohara's tests indicate that since a soft seat does not keep the body well balanced, muscles must continually work to maintain steadiness. And because the cushion distributes pressure evenly to the body, Kohara believes that the brain is deprived of the subconscious irritation that stimulates efficient thinking.

WHERE THE SPINE NEEDS SUPPORT
An X-ray photograph of an office worker shows exactly where the backrest of her chair presses against her spine. After examining this photograph, Kohara suggested that the backrest be lowered by an inch; this would remove the support from the relatively inflexible vertebrae at chest level, and give bracing to the lumbar vertebrae, the central point of spinal bending.

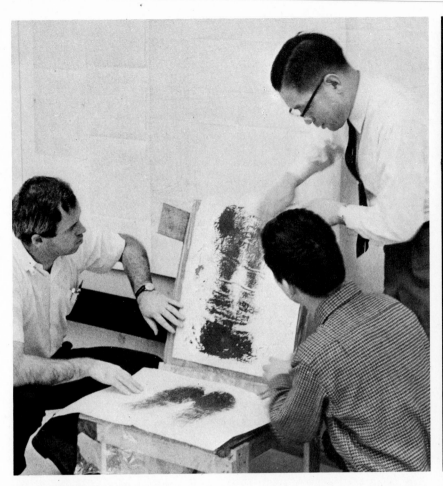

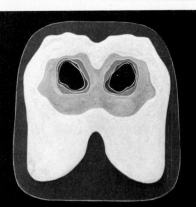

GOOD SUPPORT

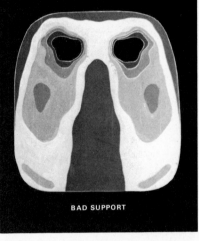

BAD SUPPORT

A CHAIR'S PATTERN OF SUPPORT

Kohara *(above, standing)* charts the distribution of body pressure on chairs by means of a simple chemical reaction. A man sits on a piece of paper that absorbs a chemical from a cloth on the chair. When the paper is dipped in another chemical, the areas of high absorption—where the body has pressed hardest—turn dark. From these papers, schematic charts of chair-support are drawn *(above, right)*. The upper chart represents the better seat design because the man's pelvic bones bear most of the pressure and his thighs are relatively unaffected.

AN ADJUSTABLE TESTING CHAIR

In designing automobile seats, human-factors engineers use a plastic skeleton and a "universal testing chair." This chair enables them to adjust the inclination of the seat, the shape of the backrest, and even the elasticity of the springs. As a result of such studies, many automobile seats now contain springs with varying degrees of recoil strength to provide firmer support at points where body pressure is greatest.

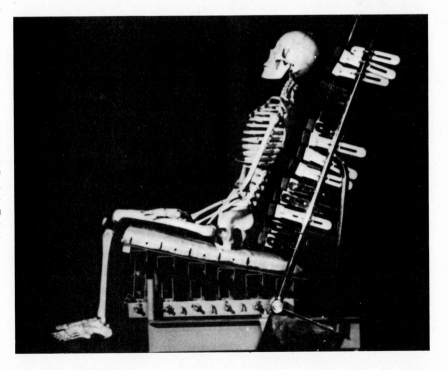

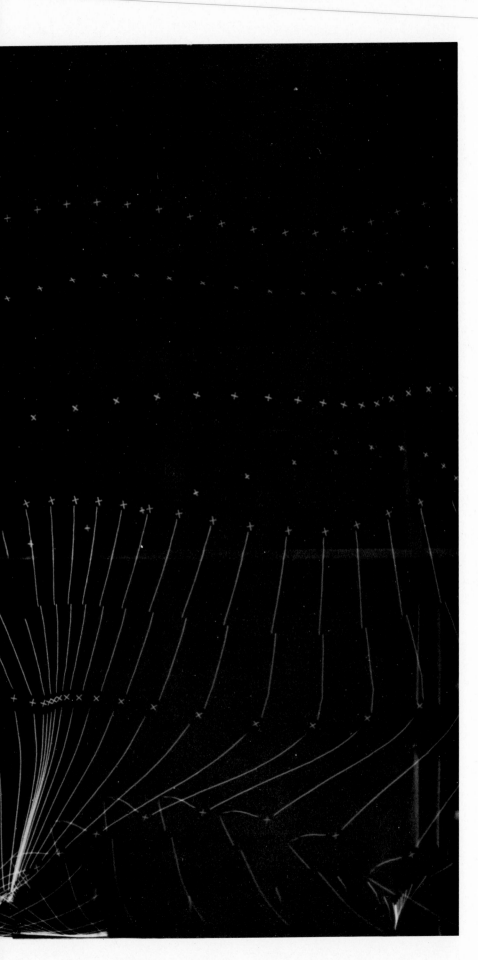

An Engineer's View of the Body

The human organism is an extraordinarily efficient and versatile device— able to discriminate between approximately 400,000 kinds of sound, able to pump more than two million quarts of blood through its own circulatory system in a year, able to plan for the future. Even the act of walking draws the deep admiration of engineers; no machine yet invented can duplicate this fluid movement. The "stick photograph" at left is one of numerous human-factors studies aimed at discovering the complex motions involved in walking. Strips of light-reflecting tape were placed at a man's hip, knee and ankle joints; a slitted disk was rotated in front of the camera lens as the man walked, producing a diagrammatic view of body motions. The photograph showed how the joints combine their rotations to achieve walking movement.

Such tests guide the design of artificial limbs. Newer limbs make use of foam rubber in the ankle joints and hydraulic devices in the knee joints to enable an amputee to walk with greater smoothness than was possible in the past. Engineers are now researching a type of artificial limb that will be equipped with small electric motors. These motors will be controlled by the nerve impulses of the amputee himself. The movements of the limb will not only look natural —they also will feel almost natural.

A GENTLE GIANT

In a demonstration of its sure touch, an Air Force apparatus clasps an egg and spoon— mimicking the motions of the operator that it carries. It can also rise to a 25-foot height on pneumatic legs, swivel, turn switches and use power tools. Since one function of the machine is to manipulate radioactive materials, the operator is protected from dangerous radiation by a two-foot-thick glass shield and lead sheathing.

Machines That Imitate Men

Late in the 19th Century, Londoners marveled at a clanking robot named Mephisto which played an excellent game of chess. Someone finally discovered that a midget was concealed inside. Today, human-factors engineers are using the same scheme— but not to hoax the public. They have found that a man can best guide extremely complicated machine movements if he is making the movements himself—rather than using buttons or levers. The 85-ton monster above, designed to tend nuclear-powered aircraft, is duplicating the arm motions of a man riding inside.

Human-factors engineers are experimenting with an even more sophisticated control system for a steel skeleton *(right)* which will enable U.S. soldiers to pick up 1,000-pound loads. Called a Man Amplifier, it will be equipped with a two-way communication system: when the operator touches or lifts an object, the skeleton transmits the pressure to him; when he responds to these signals, the steel skeleton senses the muscle action, follows it exactly, and adds the powerful push of hydraulic motors.

AN ARM OF STEEL

This steel arm is used to determine the design of joints in the Man Amplifier. Engineers concluded that the operator will have sufficient dexterity if the device has a repertoire of seven variations of elbow and shoulder movements. The operator will even be able to climb ladders.

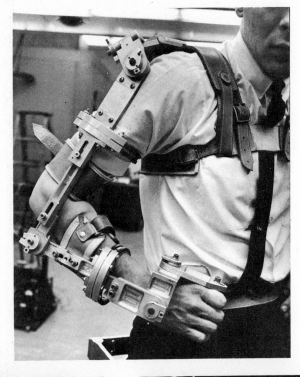

SUPERSTRENGTH IN THE MAKING

Two engineers on the Man Amplifier project bend to lift a box *(below)*. The steel skeleton on the man at right is for motion testing. The other engineer is wearing a wooden mock-up of the skeleton, complete with cylinders representing motors that will deliver nearly 20 horsepower.

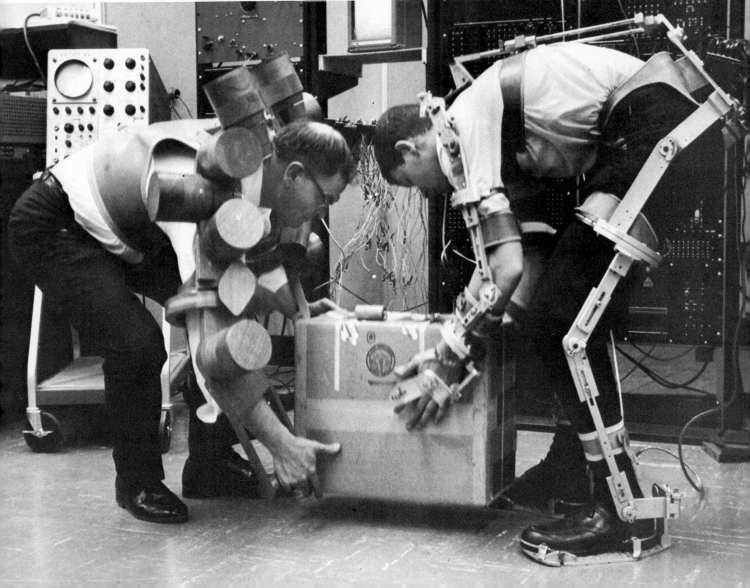

A WALL OF INSTRUMENTS

The pilot and copilot of the DC-8 jet transport must deal with hundreds of instruments and separate controls. In front of each control wheel are the principal flight instruments—the horizon indicator, gyrocompass, air speed indicator, altimeter, vertical speed indicator and the cross-pointer that locates the plane over the ground. The dials between the pilot and copilot deal with the engines. Each of the four jet engines is described by a vertical column of four instruments—adhering to the human-factors maxim that functionally related instruments should be grouped together. Great care is taken to illuminate all of the instruments evenly. The box on the floor contains the radio controls.

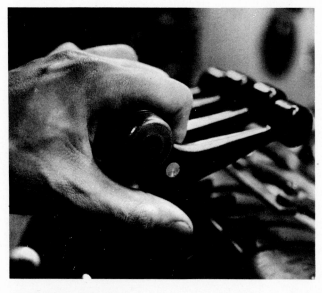

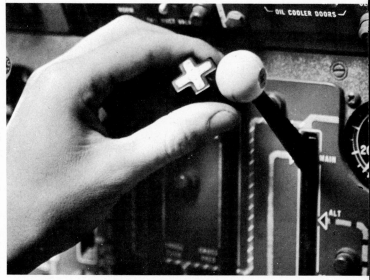

A FOURFOLD THROTTLE

The throttle controls for the four engines of the DC-8 are arranged close together so that the pilot can advance or reduce their thrusts uniformly, while still making individual engine adjustments when they are required.

A CROSS FOR CROSS-FEEDING

A cross shape designates the knob that controls cross-feeding, the flow of fuel from one tank into another. Thus, by touch as well as sight, the pilot is able to distinguish it from the round main fuel controls.

Toward Error-free Operation

Few man-machine procedures are as tension-filled as taking off or landing an airplane: the pilot must watch the runway, keep an eye out for other air traffic, check flight instruments and operate the controls. Under these conditions, it is more important to match the machine to man's brain than to his body. Since World War II thousands of human-factors engineers have been working to simplify the instruments and controls. Their changes include:

• Placing the six most important instruments in the same position in all aircraft—in front of the pilot.

• Arranging all engine instruments to point to "9 o'clock" under takeoff conditions. With this patterned display, 32 instruments can be checked in the same time it once took to check four whose needles started at different points on the dials.

• Differentiating controls by shape to make them more quickly recognizable (below).

These design changes are interim measures, in the opinion of most human-factors engineers. They believe that the future aircraft cockpit may contain as few as two instruments.

A QUICK-CHECK ALTIMETER
This DC-8 altitude indicator has three hands for hundreds, thousands and tens of thousands of feet. During landing and takeoff, a numeral appears in the striped area of the dial, giving the pilot a quick reading in hundreds of feet. Other altimeters use one hand for hundreds, inset numerals for higher figures.

ZONED TEMPERATURE GAUGES
The dual instrument for the DC-8 air-conditioning system has shaded zones along the scales to make malfunctions quickly evident. When the needles are in these zones, operations are normal. The gauge at left—for temperature of refrigerant gases—indicates overheating only because the plane is not flying.

AN AIRFOIL FOR WING FLAPS
Shaped like the device it operates, this knob sets the angle of the wing flaps. Engineers try to make the controls distinguishable by either naked or gloved hands. Controls can be identified by size as well as shape.

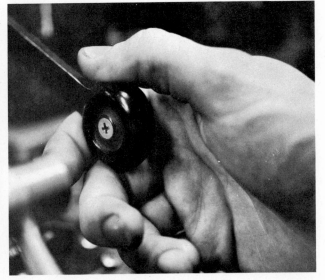

A WHEEL FOR THE LANDING GEAR
The landing gear control is recognizable both by its wheel-like shape and by the black color that distinguishes it from the nearby flap controls. Pushing down on the control lowers the wheels; pulling up raises them.

Split-second Information

The visual powers of man have not changed in thousands of years, but his rate of travel has speeded up tremendously. The jumble of signs below ignores this fact. To a driver moving at 50 or 60 miles an hour, these signs are almost useless: the print is too small; the sign placement is confusing; and the arrows seem to give conflicting directions.

From a human-factors standpoint, the European signs at right are far more effective in feeding information to the brain. Standardized shapes of the signs—a triangular sign for danger, a round sign with a slash prohibiting certain actions—immediately allow the driver to categorize the information. Human-factors tests have also shown that signs with both capital and small letters—used on the Swiss highway at right—are more easily read than those using only capital letters. Yet, in the U.S., only on a few main expressways (such as the Interstate Highway System) do signs consistently comply with recommendations of human-factors engineers.

These confusing road signs in central Ohio conform to federal standards set in 1925—which are universally regarded as obsolete.

SCHOOL CROSSING

SLIPPERY ROAD

ROAD WORKS

NO PARKING

NO TRUCKS ALLOWED

NO RIGHT TURN

A STANDARDIZED SIGN LANGUAGE
In 1949, a United Nations convention established a group of symbols for international road signs which are instantly recognizable without the need for word explanations. These have been adopted by most European nations, making motoring on that multilingual continent far less hazardous than was once the case.

A Swiss sign indicates an exit ramp and two destinations. Signs in the United States emphasize route numbers rather than destinations.

Chur

Landquart
Davos

Channeling Man's Perception

A CLOSE-UP OF THE EYE

Testing the eye movements of a "driver," the lens of a movie camera focuses on the cornea of one eye, exactly at the point where a thin beam of light is also aimed. The reflection of the light beam off the cornea traces a white track on the film, showing how the eye moves.

One of the chief jobs of human-factors engineers is to find the best sensory channel—sight, sound or touch—for any given man-machine task. In the demonstration shown on these pages, engineers are studying the effectiveness of the sight channel with a special camera that photographs eye movements. Such tests help indicate whether the information furnished a driver through the windshield and from the instrument panel is reaching him efficiently.

Sometimes the sensory channel itself must be changed. Human-factors engineers have found that sound perception often has definite advantages over sight: it may convey danger signals more effectively; it is better for simple messages; and it can be used when the visual channel is overloaded. The automobile industry is now exploring the possibility of supplementing road signs with highway radio transmitters which would issue commands over car radios to "Stop!" or "Slow down!"

Even the touch channel has some major advantages. Aircraft engineers are working on a device that through pressure will tell a pilot which direction to turn when landing. Other human-factors engineers are studying vehicle guidance systems that communicate with the operator by means of nudges and slight electric shocks.

TRACING EYE MOVEMENTS

When the subject was shown the above photograph of a car instrument panel and a street scene, her eyes focused on the speedometer and then traveled in a zigzag pattern, indicated by the numbered lines. Automobile firms are using similar photographic techniques—sometimes in moving cars—to gather information that will help position dashboard instruments.

CATCHING THE ATTENTION

As the subject of an eye-movement study is held rigidly in a head harness, a camera simultaneously photographs the reflection in the mirror *(center)* of the pictured dashboard and also the cornea of one eye as it moves from object to object. Information gained from studies like these has applications both to automobile design and to the effectiveness of advertising.

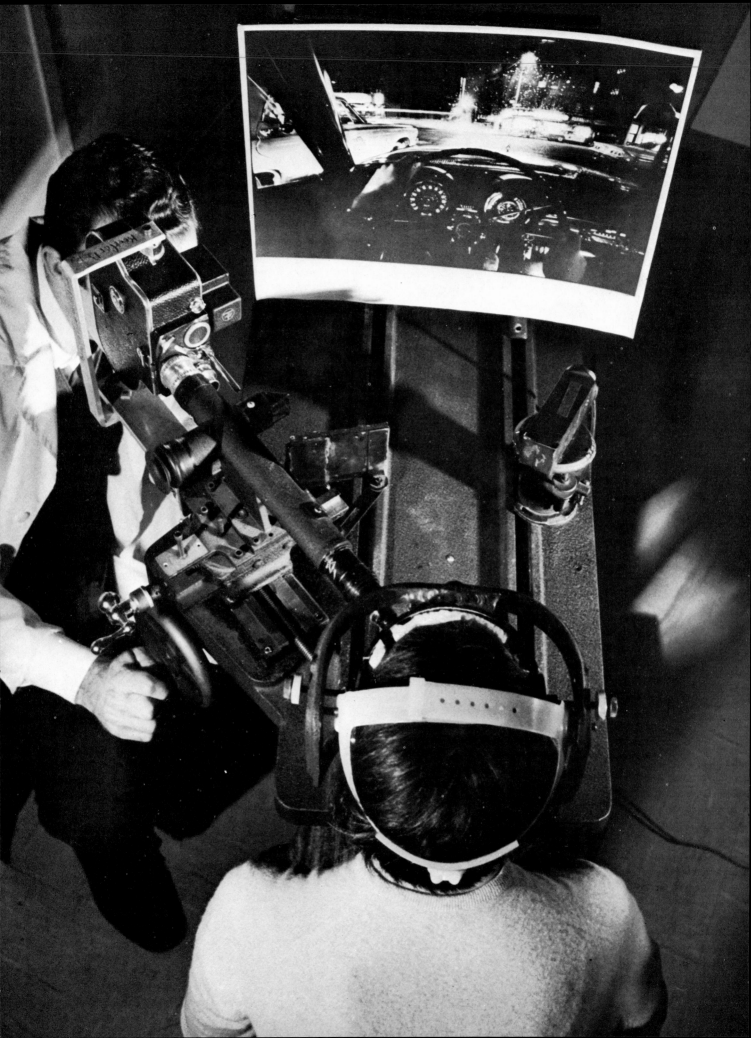

8

The Tough Problems Ahead

A computer that draws pictures is a valuable tool for engineers. Fed a mass of technical data, such a machine can produce all possible versions of a structure on a TV-like display screen—and even determine which materials are most suitable.

RECENTLY, THE PLACE OF HONOR in the kitchen of Charles and Barbara Crawshaw's home was occupied for about a year by a new kind of household appliance—a teletypewriter connected to an electronic computer in downtown Phoenix, Arizona, 10 miles away. Crawshaw, a General Electric engineer, signed up for the home computer service as an experiment and found that it made many domestic chores easier. He used it to figure out his income tax return, check household bills and reconcile his bank account—and also to calculate complex engineering problems when he brought work home at night. Mrs. Crawshaw turned to the computer for help in converting a recipe for six people into one for 11 dinner guests and for guidance in the complicated procedure of cutting and sewing intricately patterned material for living room draperies. Both the Crawshaw children used the computer to practice their arithmetic, and seven-year-old Sandra Crawshaw, the youngest member of the family, matched wits against the machine in games of ticktacktoe.

By the 21st Century—hardly more than a generation away—computer service may be so inexpensive and easy to use that it will become as common in the American home as electricity, gas, the telephone and running water. This one result of the engineer's work could make a vast change in our way of life; any child, no matter where he lived, could draw upon the entire world of education for the courses best suited to him; executives could base decisions on fresher, more accurate information, literally at their fingertips, and some people might prefer to work at home without commuting.

Even greater changes lie ahead, forced upon us by the needs and aspirations of an expanding civilization. There will be far more people—by the year 2000 the world's population will be nearly seven billion—and far more of them will dwell in cities. Four out of five people in the United States will be living in thickly settled expansions of today's city-suburbs complexes. Some of these urban areas of the future will stretch horizontally for miles beside parks and playing fields; others will rise vertically, set on stilts high above grass and shrubs.

Accompanying this unprecedented growth of urban society will be problems, some familiar and others as yet dimly appreciated, but all of them vaster in scope than ever before. More people will require far more supplies—food of course, but also manganese and vanadium for steel, silicon and selenium for electronic parts and, most of all, power to run machines. More people will demand not only new kinds of housing, but also improved transportation, varied and extensive education for both children and adults, clean air and water—and occasional respite in accessible, unspoiled countryside from the technology-oriented lives of Megalopolis.

Many of the difficult problems posed by the future will be similar to those to which the engineer has responded throughout history. It has always been his task to exploit nature economically in order to satisfy the material needs of his society. He has mined the minerals, constructed the buildings and laid out the transportation systems. He will continue to do these tasks, although perhaps in different ways. But now he is facing a new and more formidable class of problems that arise out of man's relation to his fellowman. If he can erect great cities, can the engineer help control the crime that may plague them? Can he help provide the higher levels of education needed to sustain them?

The engineer is being plunged into this broader role because now, for the first time, his tools and methods seem especially suited to it. In the modern computer he has a tool that can calculate answers to questions involving a great number of varying factors, as human questions usually do. In the technique of systems analysis he has a method that can identify the multiple factors of a problem and pull them together for submission to a computer's unbelievable swiftness in calculating the answers to involved equations.

Some hint of the great social usefulness of systems engineering in the world of tomorrow may be seen in a unique experiment carried out in California. In 1964 Governor Edmund (Pat) Brown asked engineers in the aerospace industries to focus on four of the state's most pressing political and economic problems—transportation, waste and pollution, state and local government information processing, and crime prevention. Governor Brown believed that an engineering method capable of sending an astronaut around the world in 90 minutes should be able to solve such mundane problems as air and water pollution and how to "move a father to and from work just a little bit faster."

The four studies were assigned to small groups of engineers employed by companies noted for their work on the problems of space travel: transportation went to North American Aviation, information handling to Lockheed Missiles & Space Company, waste management and pollution to Aerojet-General, and crime to Space-General, a subsidiary of Aerojet. One report achieved wide publicity—it alluded to the Watts area of Los Angeles as a "susceptible" trouble spot a month before the 1965 eruption of racial violence in that section of the city. But the studies' real value was their demonstration of the way that systems engineering can provide a fresh look at big problems.

Equations for a state

The systems analysis method followed in the California studies was the same as the one that the engineering firms use in designing spacecraft. The entire state was viewed as a system, and the complex overall problem to be examined was divided into component parts. Then each component element was translated into mathematical representations, called models or submodels, whose characteristics were expressed in formulas and equations.

It may seem impossible to reduce such a vague concept as, say, transportation, to the niceties of mathematical equations. But similar problems were solved mathematically during World War II: equations showed how to lay down bombs on a target so that they would have maximum effect while keeping the planes in a formation least vulnerable to enemy attack by antiaircraft shells and fighter planes.

If the imponderables of war can be calculated, so can transportation. Numerical values can be assigned to land cost, to the average distance and frequency of trips, to construction expenses, to population growth and to other factors that enter into the potential usefulness of a transportation network. These factors must then be weighted according to relative significance, fitted into the equations and fed to a computer. Because the computer can handle so many calculations so rapidly, large numbers of alternatives may be compared—an express highway versus a subway versus a monorail, one route against another, even the effect of refusal to build new transportation lines.

The results will indicate, in gambler's fashion, the most practical way of achieving the desired effect. They will, that is, if the key factors have been correctly identified, weighted and compared. This is a very big "if," and the validity of the outcome depends greatly on the skill of the systems engineer who makes the analysis.

The trend in transportation

In the transportation study, several mathematical models were set up to represent the problem of moving people and goods from one part of California to another. Among the factors involved were the distribution of population, the use of land in various areas, the geographic setup of the economy and the demands for transportation facilities to meet requirements of population, land use and economy, as well as the need for travel to recreation areas. The engineers' calculations produced the valuable, but alarming, predictions that California's daily movement of people would double in the next 25 years and increase five times in the next 50 years. Moreover, the transportation of goods—mail, food and manufactured commodities—would triple in 25 years and go up seven to 10 times in 50 years. Obviously today's transportation concepts are inadequate to meet such a heavy demand. The suggestions put forward for coping with California's looming transportation problems give a lively picture of what engineers, especially those in the field of civil engineering, will be likely to do for the world of tomorrow.

Because land will be needed for so many purposes there will be little surface room in urban areas for the expansion of highways. Jack Jones, the North American engineer who directed the transportation study, foresees tunnels as an alternative to overcrowded and costly highways. Jet-propelled trains, too, could run through tunnels at high speeds. Jones believes that consumer goods, particularly perishable farm products, will be carried to markets in underground pipelines, making it possible for housewives to buy tree-ripened fruits a few hours after they are picked. He also expects that pipelines on the ocean bed will carry oil from California to Alaska and fresh water from Alaska to California.

The engineers who investigated California's pollution problems found that the approach taken by the state was absolutely contrary to the cardinal rule of the systems engineer: first establish the output desired

TELEGRAM

```
RECIPE     15:30   FRI.

HOW MANY PERSONS DOES YOUR RECIPE SERVE? 6
HOW MANY PERSONS DO YOU WISH TO SERVE? 11
HOW MANY INGREDIENTS ARE REQUIRED? 5

FOR EACH INGREDIENT ENTER THE ORIGINAL AMOUNT
    INGREDIENT NUMBER 1    ? 1.25
    INGREDIENT NUMBER 2    ? 3.75
    INGREDIENT NUMBER 3    ? 5
    INGREDIENT NUMBER 4    ? 12
    INGREDIENT NUMBER 5    ? 4.333

USE 2.29167 PARTS OF INGREDIENT NUMBER 1
USE 6.875   PARTS OF INGREDIENT NUMBER 2
USE 9.16667 PARTS OF INGREDIENT NUMBER 3
USE 22      PARTS OF INGREDIENT NUMBER 4
USE 7.94383 PARTS OF INGREDIENT NUMBER 5

TIME:  12 SECS.

RYE
```

COOKING BY COMPUTER was one of the tasks assigned to a Phoenix, Arizona, housewife when she participated in an experiment in time-sharing—a technique engineers have recently developed to allow a number of people to use the same computer simultaneously. To communicate with the computer, Mrs. Charles Crawshaw typed data *(color)* on a teletypewriter installed in her kitchen. (The computer's replies are shown in black.) In this case the computer was instructed to expand a chicken recipe for six people so that it would feed 11. It made the conversions to a degree of accuracy far surpassing the most meticulous cook's measuring ability, and signed off in 12 seconds.

from the system. Instead of determining the output—how pure its air, water and soil should be—and then designing a system to meet that requirement, the state was trying to cope with the input, the appalling increase in waste matter. As one space expert pointedly remarked to Governor Brown: "They didn't come to us and say, 'Design Gemini and we'll figure out how to use it later.'"

The engineers concluded that if cities in the San Francisco and Central Valley areas want cleaner air, water and land, they will have to increase their expenditures for pollution control more than five times by 1990. Even if a decision is made to accept an increased level of pollution in 1990, the cost of waste disposal will triple because of population growth.

Cleaner fuels, cleaner air

This dismal forecast, however, could be tempered by technical developments that could change the sources of the wastes. Air pollution, for instance, comes largely from the processes now used for converting fuels into useful energy—into home heat, electricity, vehicle power. The pollution in a city such as Los Angeles arises about equally from the smoke of home and industrial furnaces and from the exhaust of automobiles. However, increasingly closer to reality are alternative means of producing energy requirements without contaminating the atmosphere. Nuclear power plants are expected to provide 18 per cent of the nation's electricity by 1980. Many experts believe that about half the new plants being built at the end of the century will harness the energy released by the splitting of atoms; older, coal-burning units will gradually be phased out. A dozen such nuclear power plants spotted around the country, each having a capacity of perhaps 60 million kilowatts (as against Grand Coulee Dam's 1,974,000 kilowatts) could supply nearly half the electricity needed by the entire United States. If one of these generating stations were placed on Mount Wilson, above Los Angeles, its discarded heat might even be guided into the atmosphere to play a role in modifying the weather. The rising currents, according to this speculation, might help lift the smog-causing layer of warm air so frequently found over Los Angeles. Farther in the future, but even more enticing to engineers for its potential economies, is the prospect of useful power derived from the fusion rather than the fission of atoms—in effect, from tamed H-bombs.

Widespread application of nuclear power would greatly reduce the demand for oil and coal to generate electricity, thus eliminating in many areas these troublesome causes of air pollution. Nuclear engines, however, seem unlikely ever to become practical for running cars and trucks. That need may be supplied by electricity derived from another source—a different type of battery called the fuel cell, which has provided most of the power for the Command and Service Modules on the Apollo flights of astronauts to the moon.

The fuel cell would give to automobiles all the benefits of electric

"The computer sent me. You're being replaced!"

GOVERNMENT BY COMPUTER was spoofed in this 1964 cartoon after California's Governor Edmund G. Brown turned to systems engineers for help with four growing problems: transportation, records centralization, crime and waste control. The studies were completed in 1965 and the state has implemented some of the suggestions, including computerized systems for retaining information on driver's licenses, auto registrations and stolen cars.

drive—light weight, quiet operation, efficiency—plus some advantages of its own. It is a battery that never runs down. It continues to produce electricity through chemical combination of two reactants as long as they are fed to it. The most economical fuels are hydrocarbons (such as gasoline), now being tested in some experimental cells. But the easiest fuel to use—and the one employed in the Apollo power system—is hydrogen. Hydrogen, when combined with oxygen, produces water, an absolutely harmless waste. Moreover, this waste could even serve as a source of fresh reactants, since the fuel cell could be run backwards, consuming electricity while it separates water into hydrogen and oxygen. A car with a fuel-cell power plant could be plugged into a household's electric supply at night; by morning the car would be fueled for the day's trips.

The search for new sources of power, materials and food is part of the engineer's continuing effort to provide for the needs of society, which grow with the growth of population. Where will the new supplies come from? Already engineers are exploring ways to tap the resources of the sea, of remote land areas—perhaps even of the moon.

Farmers and miners of the sea

The sea is one of the most fertile sources of materials and food, according to a group of experts who were questioned by T. J. Gordon and Olaf Helmer of the Rand Corporation in 1964. Some of these experts implied that the oceans may become the scene of so much engineering activity that nations will lay claim to particular water-covered areas of the earth, exercising the same sovereignty over ocean bottoms that they now have over dry land. Other experts predict that fish will be herded and raised in offshore corrals, like cattle in Texas or Wyoming; kelp and seaweed will be cultivated by frogmen farmers. One rich source of food from the sea, which may be a staple part of tomorrow's diet is *Chlorella pyrenoidosa*, algae so prolific that an underwater field can produce 200 times more protein than a soybean planting of the same size.

The water of the ocean is already being treated chemically to recover magnesium, bromine and other valuable substances. Still to be mined extensively is the sea bottom which, particularly on the deep floor of the Pacific, is strewn with nodules of manganese, copper, nickel, cobalt and deposits of materials used in portland cement. The nodules are porous and light; most are about the size of a potato, although some weigh almost a ton. Similar in origin to pearls, the nodules are formed by accretions of ore on a core of sand or other small object.

Because of the high metal content of the nodules, mining in the ocean may prove more economical than on land. Approximately 50 per cent of each nodule would be marketable, in contrast to about 2 per cent of today's land-mined nickel and copper ores. Handling costs would be comparatively low, and inexpensive sea transportation could carry the ore directly from the undersea mining site to the markets of the world. The ocean seems to hold the reassuring answer to the long-held fears of grave

OUR RESTLESS POPULATION, which, as this graph shows, has moved steadily from rural to urban areas since 1790, raises tough problems for engineers. Their new technique of systems analysis is already being applied to safeguards against crime and to decrease air and water pollution for the 75 per cent of all Americans who are expected to live in cities by 1980.

shortages of food and minerals as sources found on land are exhausted.

This prospective abundance of materials and power could work radical changes in improving the conditions of life for broad areas of society. Equally significant could be the effects of the engineer's application of his technique of systems analysis to political and economic problems. But such engineering efforts would have only indirect influence on the way ordinary people conduct their everyday affairs. This would not be true of another development: the engineer's mastery of his unique tool, the electronic computer.

"If any single item of hardware is destined to take command of the look and lilt of urban life over the next 35 years, as the ubiquitous automobile did during the past 35, that item almost surely is the electronic computer," one prophet has written. "First, and unquestionably, the computer will complete its take-over as the central nervous system of municipalities, businesses, libraries and other storage centers for information. Later, for better or worse, its nerve ends at least will invade the home."

Already computers are inexpensive for business use. A versatile machine, like an IBM System/360, costs as little as two dollars per hour to use, and the average engineering problem occupies less than a minute of its time. An ordinary domestic problem—like the conversion of recipes for Mrs. Crawshaw—would take perhaps a few seconds, and computers could take on such homely tasks if they could be connected inexpensively to every home.

A robot around the house

Similar tasks of everyday life are bound to be taken over by computers when such service is generally available. Housework, and probably baby-watching, will be handled in the 21st Century by multiarmed computerized robots. An IBM official said recently that most of the technology for the design of such robots has already been solved. The device would run the vacuum cleaner, empty ashtrays, scrub bathroom floors, dump garbage and trash into wall inlets, pick up fallen magazines and newspapers and rearrange disordered furniture with more meticulous efficiency than most human employees.

Computerized banking service will make money and checks unnecessary. A housewife who wants to pay a bill will dial a code number for the store, another series of numbers representing the amount of the bill and a third number identifying her bank account. Without a word of conversation, the bank's computer will transfer the amount from her account to the account of the store. When she is out shopping, she could present a credit-charge card. Placed in a slot in the cash register when the sale is rung up, it would automatically instruct the customer's bank account

URBAN BELTS *(below)* result from the heavy concentration of population in cities of the U.S., especially in the Northeast and on the West Coast *(shaded above)*. Space between existing cities, such as Los Angeles and San Diego *(below)* or Boston and Washington *(below, right)*, is gradually being filled up, solidifying the cities into a single urban region. Engineers are already helping to meet the problems of such areas, and one example is the development of new types of high-speed vehicles for mass intercity transportation.

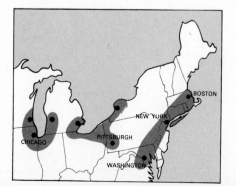

to make payment and credit the store's account with the correct sum.

These new services will certainly affect the comfort and convenience of innumerable people. But the greatest impact of the computer on the ordinary person will be felt in its influence on his education. Few educators think that the computer can eliminate regular trips to a classroom, since group activity is essential to learning. What the computer *can* do is multiply many times over the kinds of training that will be available and the kinds of students who will take that training. If one child in a small town elected Swedish for his modern-language study, he could nonetheless join a course by punching a few keys on a keyboard. If his term paper demanded esoteric information, he could get an answer to his query in seconds from the repositories of knowledge in Washington, D.C., in Cambridge, Massachusetts, or even in Stockholm. For adults, the computer would bring any training that might be desired, at a time that was convenient.

Perils in a data capsule

The rosy world promised by the clicking printout of the computer may leave very ugly blemishes, which engineers are quick to point out. One of the most distressing potential effects of fully computerized living is the threat to personal privacy. Records of a man's credit history, medical ailments, law violations and military service, now widely dispersed and generally inaccessible, may be gathered together in one compact and easily available data capsule under the computerized records system of a future government. "Unless appropriate precautions are planned now," comments Paul Armer in a Rand Corporation report, "an unscrupulous individual would be able to turn up scandal and defamatory information (where it exists) with comparative ease. . . . The basic question is the wisdom of all aspects of a person's past life being a completely open book."

Loss of our personal rights, restrictions on our choice of actions, failures of "foolproof" machines—all these are nightmares with their basis in harsh reality. The engineer recognizes them as the new problems that, inevitably, accompany every solution to an old problem. The balancing of dangers against benefits has always been his task. He does not forget his ancient predecessor, the first man to build a fire. That unknown genius knew he could get burned, but he also may have realized that he was changing the course of his species toward what would be called civilization. The engineer helped make civilization. He continues to extend it, to make the 20th Century, in the words of the historian Arnold Toynbee, "the first age since the dawn of civilization, some five or six thousand years back, in which people dared to think it practicable to make the benefits of civilization available to the whole human race."

Designs for
the Year 2000

Even as he works at solving the many technical problems of today, the engineer is thinking ahead and shaping dramatic new concepts that someday may be as commonplace as the electric light, the telephone and the jet plane. By the year 2000, if systems now under development are perfected, men—some with damaged hearts replaced by transistorized pumps—will travel from city to city on trackless trains at supersonic speeds, and communicate quickly with any point on earth—or other planets—by means of elaborate networks of beamed light. Their food may be grown on what is now wasteland—barren desert and tundra, converted to rich granaries by a controlled climate beneath enormous inflated domes. They will live for long periods in underwater houses, emerging to move freely about the ocean's floor and to bring forth the vast mineral wealth buried there: minerals to be smelted with the harnessed power of the sun. Given the challenge, the funds and the time, the engineer can overcome the technical problems that stand between any of these dreams and reality. In most cases he is, in effect, only waiting for the scope of the problem to reach the dimensions of his solution.

BUILDING A NEW HEART
Listening to a simulated heartthrob, William Akers of Rice University checks a plastic heart valve. The valve, here being tested with colored fluid of the same consistency as blood, is designed to replace a damaged natural valve in regulating blood flow between heart chambers. It is one step toward the realization of a complete artificial heart—and perhaps other human organs as well.

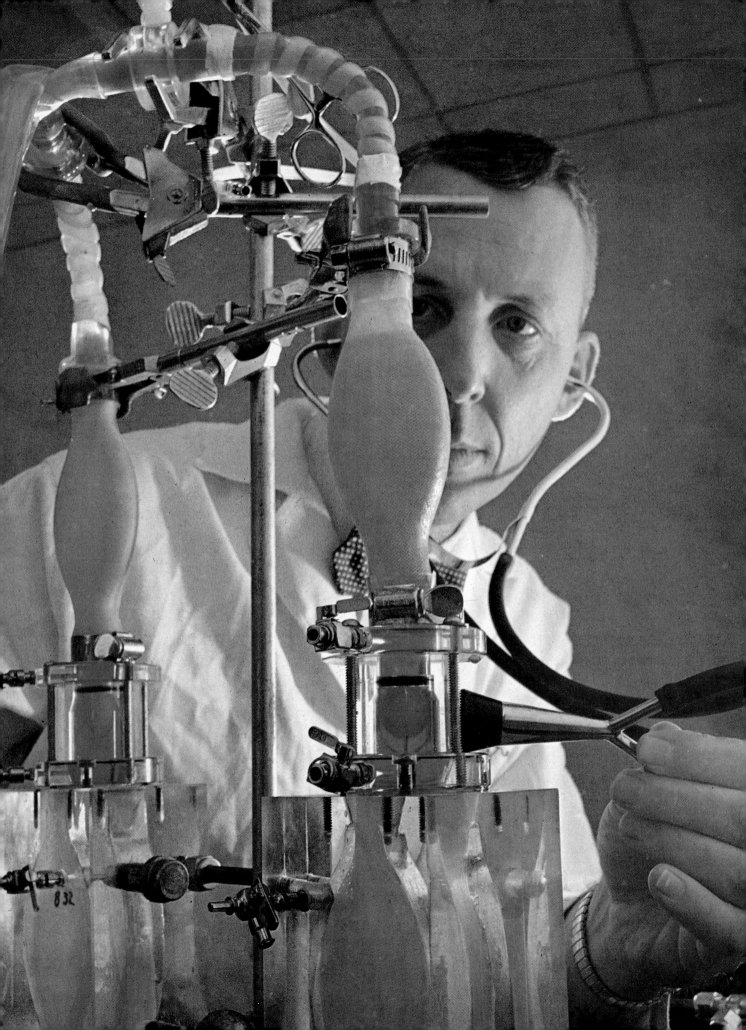

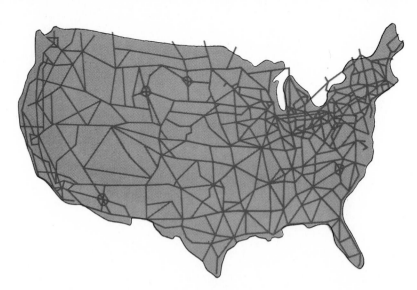

This proposed network of laser lines could accommodate all communications in the U.S.

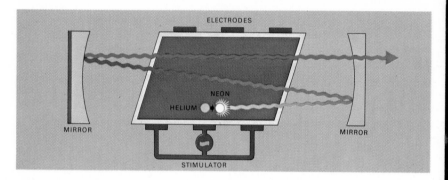

BUILDING THE LASER BEAM

In the simplified drawing shown above, the creation of a laser beam begins with a mixture of helium and neon gases sealed in a glass tube. When the helium atoms are electrically stimulated, they collide with neon atoms, raising the neon's energy level. The neon atoms release their excess energy as bits of light that reflect between the two mirrors outside the tube; gaining energy with each rebound, the light of many millions of such bits finally becomes so intense that it penetrates through the thin silver backing of the mirror at right, emerging as a laser beam.

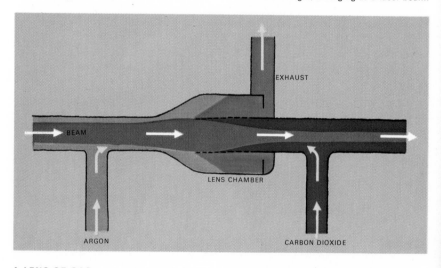

A LENS OF GAS

To maintain the intensity of a laser beam projected through a half-inch-diameter pipe requires the presence of a "gas lens" every 20 or 30 feet to refocus the beam. The lens, shown in this schematic drawing, is a mixture of argon and carbon dioxide gases introduced into the lens chamber by a suction device. The beam is refocused as it passes through the two gases, i.e., it is compressed again to its original thinness. These lenses can be used to change a laser beam's direction; to make a 45° turn necessitates a gas lens every two to four feet.

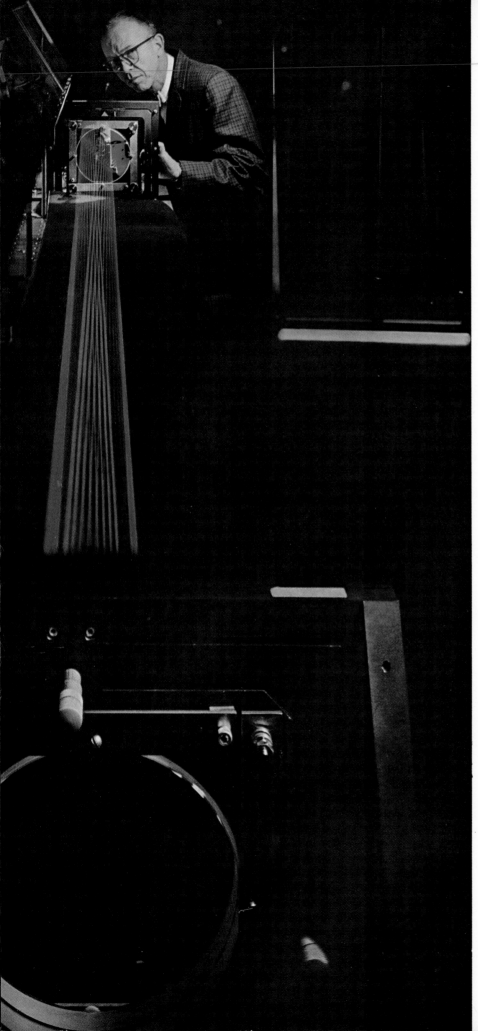

The Light That Carries Sound

By the year 2000, elaborate communications systems will link the cities of the world by radio, television and telephone; other systems will carry computerized information to homes, offices and schools, and will even permit computers to question each other. Much of this immense communication load may be carried on highly concentrated laser beams—light reduced to the width of a pencil lead.

Not only do laser beams travel at the same high speed—186,000 miles per second—as the microwaves which now carry the bulk of the world's long-distance communications, but their higher frequencies enable them to carry far more information than can microwaves. With the increasing demand for communications already taxing the present cable and microwave networks, engineers are working to iron out the many problems that now restrict the laser to experimental use.

Though the laser has a tremendous range—beams have been bounced off the moon—the dust, fog and rain of the earth's atmosphere dissipate its beam, thereby weakening it. One solution envisioned by engineers is to run the beam through a web of thin pipes *(upper left, opposite)*. The potential of this network would be enormous. In a recent experiment, a laser beam carried the signals of seven New York City TV stations for a short distance. It was hardly a fair test. Properly utilized, just a single laser beam might carry simultaneously every television program in the world— and every telephone call as well.

TWO MILES IN 10 FEET
An engineer adjusts one of the mirrors that bounce a laser beam back and forth a thousand times in 10 feet—a total beam length of two miles. By "folding" a long beam into this laboratory-sized space, engineers can measure distortions that might otherwise escape detection.

AS SWIFT AS A JET

A model of a jet-propelled train appears as a red blur racing up a plastic tube under the watchful eye of its inventor, Joseph V. Foa of George Washington University. One of the major problems encountered in such a system is the resistance set up by air trapped in the tube ahead of the vehicle; the typical subway train, for example, which must push forward the entire column of air in its path, is limited in its speed by this resistance. By installing a jet engine in the nose of this train, Foa not only was able to lower air resistance by rapidly transferring air from the front to the rear, but also was able to use the same air for swift propulsion. Sealing the tunnel ahead of the train, as Foa is doing with his model, helps too, for by preventing outside air from entering the tunnel it reduces the amount of air the train must displace.

A Flying Train inside a Tube

In 1939 a fast train trip from Washington to New York took three hours and 35 minutes; by 1970, the time had been cut to two hours and 30 minutes. In 30 years the same journey may be made in an hour aboard a train that literally flies through a tube at speeds of 250 to 400 mph. Convinced that the train is still the most efficient method of moving multitudes from point to point, aeronautical engineer Joseph V. Foa is trying to graft aviation technology onto the railroad system, basically unchanged for a century. Instead of running on tracks, however, Foa's vehicle, with its six air-cushion pods, would run inside a steel tube, never touching the walls except when starting and stopping. Motive power would be supplied by a jet engine that scoops up air from in front of the train, compresses it and expels it rearward to create the same sort of thrust that propels a jet airplane. The train, devised to travel between large cities, may succeed in providing the cheap, superswift and efficient mass transportation that has for so long eluded our conventional passenger railways.

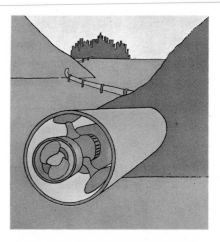

REPLACING RAILROAD TRACKS
Like some huge pipeline, the 15-foot-diameter tubes of the flying train, seen in this cutaway sketch, could be tunneled through mountains and carried over rivers—or, to avoid curves and gain stability, laid about 500 feet underground.

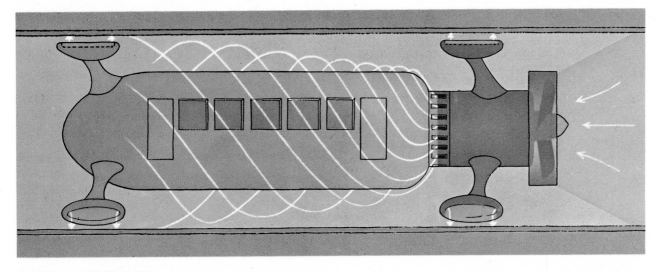

THE TRAIN OF TOMORROW
The flying train, illustrated in simplified form above, is planned as a 130-foot vehicle carrying 104 passengers. To propel it, the turbines of a jet engine whip air from the front into a powerful spiraling thrust rearward. Some of the air is ducted to the train's six pods, from which it rushes out to form nine-inch air cushions between the train and the tube walls. The wheelless train slides on these frictionless cushions, which can be adjusted to lower or lift the vehicle for arrivals and departures. A different version of the flying train, that could travel from coast to coast at supersonic speeds, is tested in model form below, substituting water for air in order to demonstrate its thrust patterns.

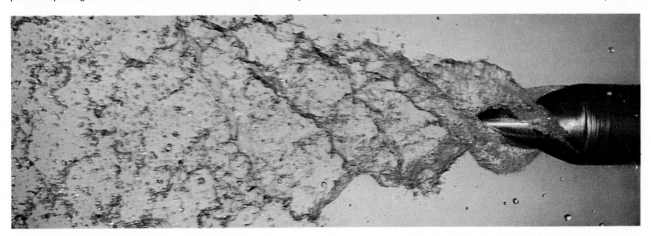

A Dome Fit
for a City

Ever since man first moved out of a cave for the comfort of a rudely built hut, he has been trying to protect ever-greater areas from the weather. Now, with the development of huge, air-supported structures such as this radome at Andover, Maine, which houses a ground station for global communications satellites, engineers may be on the threshold of attaining total shelter. In a domed city, inhabitants could enjoy springlike weather all year long through climate control. By the same token, farmers in Canada might be able to grow oranges on domed acres.

The air-supported dome, prefabricated from lightweight strips of coated synthetic material only 1/12 of an inch thick, needs neither beams nor walls. The pressure created by small blowers no bigger than those used in women's hair dryers is sufficient to support it.

Without an air-supported fabric structure, this satellite communications station would have been impractical. Its antenna requires protection from rain, snow and wind, but a building of steel and concrete would have blocked the radio waves that the station sends and receives.

AIR VERSUS AIR

Maintaining enough pressure *(arrows)* to support the Andover radome's 120,000 square feet of rubber-coated Dacron, weighing 30 tons, usually requires air pumped from only one or two blowers. As many as five may be used during high winds or heavy snowstorms, when distortion and tearing might occur if the fabric was not kept taut by increased interior pressure. All radome entrances are protected from leaks by air locks.

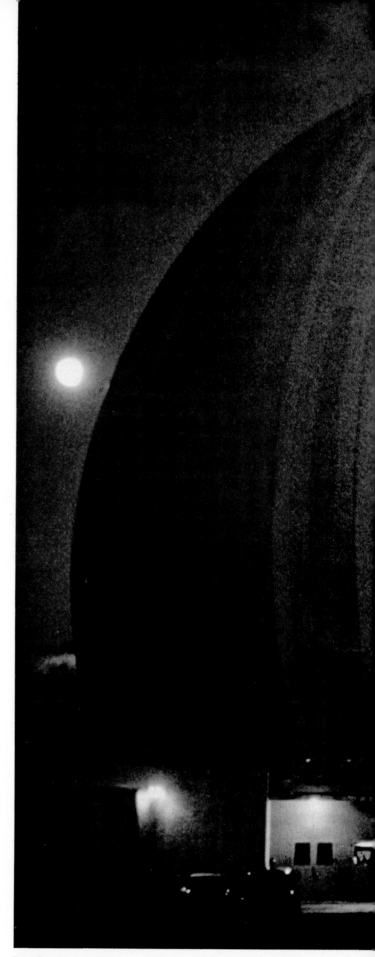

Dwarfing surrounding automobiles, the Andover dome—largest of its type

in the world—is 160 feet high with a diameter of 210 feet. The dome's tough synthetic-fabric skin is firmly anchored to a concrete base.

A Look at Tomorrow's City

The planned city of the year 2000 may be a clean, uncluttered place without slums or traffic problems.

This is the goal of city planners like architect-engineer Constantinos A. Doxiadis *(right)*, who created a city of the future in the early 1960s when he designed Islamabad, the new capital of Pakistan. The city's plan *(below)* attempts to restore the "human dimension" now lacking in most large urban centers—the ability to accommodate all groups, from millionaires to factory workers, comfortably in locations of their choice.

The most important component in Doxiadis' plan is growth by systematic decentralization, a sharp break with the traditional concentric pattern of city growth *(opposite, top),* which results in a core of "downtown" industry and commerce ringed by slums inhabited by low-income workers. Doxiadis has substituted an "axis of growth" for the restrictive core. In his plan a broad band of population extends in a single direction from the administrative base and incorporates many communities, which are set up as needed. These interrelated cities-within-a-city are linked together by wide boulevards running the length of the axis.

As other cities rise from similarly engineered plans, many urbanites of the future may be able to walk to work, to school or to a shopping center along pleasant, treelined streets.

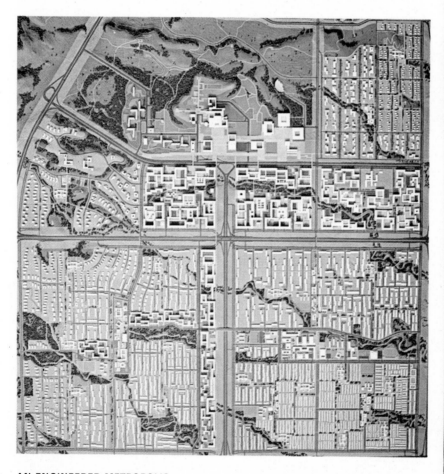

AN ENGINEERED METROPOLIS
Part of Islamabad's master plan shows the main boulevard leading down the center from the Pakistani government buildings *(top)* along the main axis of growth. On either side of the axis, the grid patterns divide communities into smaller and smaller neighborhoods. A number of the streets in Islamabad's residential sections have dead ends, designed to reduce through traffic.

THE UNPLANNED CITY

Most major cities have evolved as a series of unplanned concentric rings, built around a core of industry and commerce. The rings represent surrounding residential areas. As industry expands, it invades the nearest residential ring; the middle and high income groups move to the city's outskirts, leaving behind only the low income groups and setting the stage for a slum.

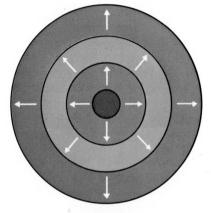

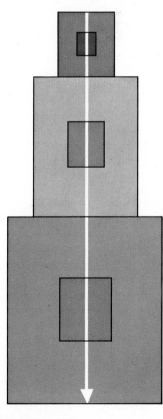

THE PLANNED CITY

The basic concept of the Doxiadis city (diagram above) rests on spacing business and industry along a preordained route that avoids existing residential sections. Instead, complete neighborhoods are added along the axis as extensions of the city. This plan is being carried out in Islamabad, seen in the model at left. Designer Doxiadis indicates its main axis of growth.

New Settlers on the Ocean Floor

In their quest for knowledge, marine scientists and engineers are transforming the sea into just another place to live and work. Their success at undersea living is being measured in such pioneering programs as Project Tektite, a joint venture of U.S. government, industry and universities, off St. John, Virgin Islands. The basic aims of Tektite were achieved in 1969 when four scientists demonstrated that they could live and work for a full two months in and around a specially designed habitat 50 feet below the surface; they remained in excellent physical and mental health despite having to share limited quarters and breathe an oxygen-nitrogen mixture under pressure. The habitat consists of two 18-by-12½-foot cylinders, connected by a tunnel, housing a laboratory, living quarters and supporting equipment; power, communications, air and drinking water are supplied from shore through a 975-foot life support line. A second series of missions conducted in 1970 has provided valuable experience that may aid other teams in exploring the resources of the continental shelves.

Readying their habitat for occupancy, aquanauts remove a porthole cover, check life support lines and inspect a shark cage.

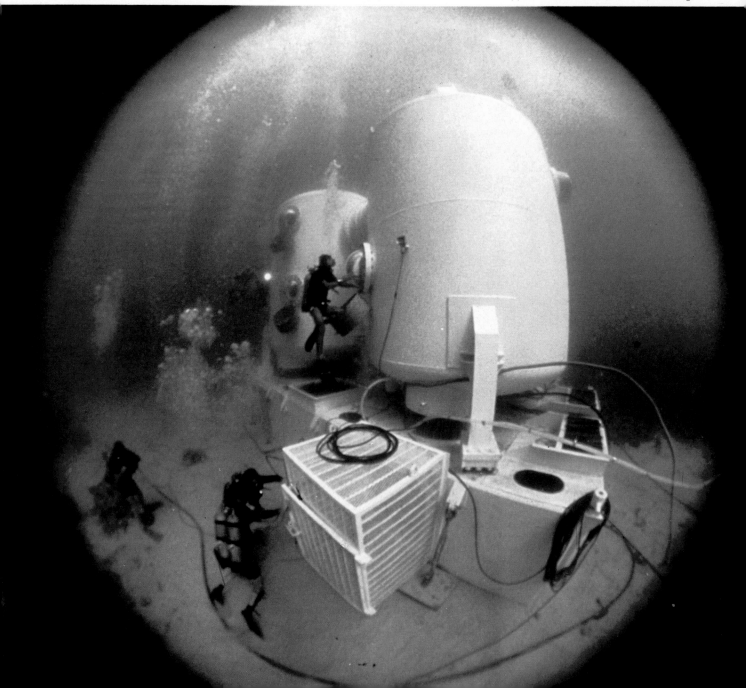

TEKTITE OBSERVED

Keeping a 24-hour watch topside, scientists monitor the Tektite crew from a control room in a van overlooking the sea. Their links with the underwater encampment include closed-circuit television and microphones, enabling them to follow all aspects of the team's undersea life.

A SHELTER IN THE SEA

An aquanaut *(below)* telephones the surface from a special cage, having used his scuba tank to fill its plastic dome with air so that he can breathe and speak at the same time. The cage, one of five shelters near the habitat, offers refuge from sharks and houses extra oxygen tanks.

ALL THE COMFORTS OF HOME

Life in the habitat is reasonably comfortable, as can be seen in the two pictures at right. Sitting at the table in their carpeted living quarters, four members of a research team enjoy a meal from the provisions in their refrigerator. (They also receive occasional home-cooked meals from their wives via a transfer capsule that shuttles from the surface to the habitat.) Books, radio, TV and games take care of leisure hours.

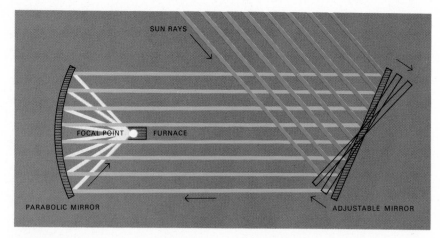

Harnessing the Heat of the Sun

The extent to which a country can utilize its natural resources provides a basic measurement of its economic well-being, and engineers are always on the alert for new ways to extract power. Among the most radical of current efforts are projects to harness the sun's heat for industrial use. At present, France leads the world in exploring the potential of solar furnaces for scientific and industrial purposes. Such furnaces may offer underdeveloped countries that are poor in power but wealthy in minerals and sunlight a chance to make high-performance alloys for industry.

CONCENTRATING THE SUN'S RAYS
Experimental solar furnaces sponsored by the French government have shown how effectively the sun's rays can be used for high-temperature heating to produce entirely new materials and contaminant-free products. In the one shown here, a flat, 1,453-square-foot mirror, oriented by photoelectric cells, swivels on its axis to catch the sun's rays, reflecting them onto a 968-square-foot parabolic mirror. This mirror concentrates and reflects the rays so that they converge at the focal point of the furnace, creating temperatures up to 5,400° F.

THE HOTTEST SPOT
Holding a thick iron bar at the solar furnace's focal point, a French engineer watches with his assistants as the sun's concentrated rays burn through the iron in 15 seconds. The furnace was installed at Montlouis in the Pyrenees, which has up to 200 days of pure sunshine a year.

3,500 REFLECTING MIRRORS
Workmen adjust some of the 3,500 tiny mirrors that make up the parabolic reflector. By tilting the mirrors, which are concave in shape, engineers are able to vary the concentration of the sun's rays and thus the heat of the furnace.

Great Engineers of Recent Centuries

WITHIN THE LAST 200 YEARS engineers have produced a host of machines, techniques and concepts that are the bases of our present technological civilization. Some of these engineers have been originators like the Wright brothers, who developed the first powered airplane. But most of them have been men like James Watt or Henry Ford, who possessed the vision and skill to refine an existing invention to the point where it became practical. The brief sketches that follow outline the major contributions made to the world by 28 great engineers —from the Industrial Revolution to World War II.

JAMES BRINDLEY

(English, 1716-1772)
Brindley, a self-educated engineer, designed a network of shipping canals which served as England's major industrial transportation system until the advent of railroads in the early 19th Century.

JOHN SMEATON

(English, 1724-1792)
Smeaton is recognized for his pioneer work in the field of civil engineering. He planned harbors, dams, canals, drainage works and bridges, and won fame for building a lighthouse which for 120 years survived the storms that sweep England's Eddystone Rock.

SMEATON

SIR RICHARD ARKWRIGHT

(English, 1732-1792)
Arkwright developed a water-powered spinning machine which revolutionized the cotton industry. So great was its influence in bringing workers out of their homes and into factories that Arkwright is credited with fathering the modern factory system.

ARKWRIGHT

JAMES WATT

(Scottish, 1736-1819)
Although Watt is commonly believed to have invented the steam engine, his principal contribution was developing a condenser which made existing engines more efficient. Later, in partnership with a manufacturer, Matthew Boulton, Watt opened a factory where he continued to build and improve steam engines.

WATT

THOMAS TELFORD

(Scottish, 1757-1834)
An extraordinarily versatile civil engineer, Telford is renowned for his bridges and for the highways with which he laced Scotland, England and Wales. A pioneer in iron bridge construction, he built the first successful long-span suspension bridge, across the Menai Strait in Wales.

ELI WHITNEY

(American, 1765-1825)
Best known for his invention of the cotton gin, Whitney also pioneered in the manufacture of interchangeable parts, a concept that led to modern mass production.

WHITNEY

HENRY MAUDSLAY

(English, 1771-1831)
Industrialization in the late 18th Century created a pressing need for accurate machine tools. Maudslay developed many of the tools which met this demand, including a metal-working lathe and a micrometer accurate to an unprecedented 0.0001 inch.

GEORGE STEPHENSON

(English, 1781-1848)
Stephenson is generally credited with establishing the steam railway, which dominated inland transportation for almost a century. He built the first practical steam locomotives, the first general freight and passenger railroad and, with his son, designed many tracks and bridges for his trains.

STEPHENSON

BRUNEL

ISAMBARD K. BRUNEL

(English, 1806-1859)
Brunel designed the *Great Western*, the first steamship that made regular Atlantic crossings, and the *Great Eastern*, the vessel which laid the Atlantic telegraph cable of 1866. Earlier in his career Brunel worked on tunnels, railroads and bridges.

JOHN ROEBLING

(German-American, 1806-1869)
One of the world's greatest geniuses at bridge building, Roebling developed and also manufactured the steel-wire cable that has made it possible to build safe, long-span suspension bridges. His outstanding projects included the Niagara Falls suspension bridge and the Brooklyn Bridge crossing New York City's East River; the latter, also a suspension bridge, was his last work, for he was fatally injured while supervising its construction. His son finished the project.

ROEBLING

CYRUS McCORMICK

(American, 1809-1884)
McCormick set off the mechanization of agriculture by developing and manufacturing a successful reaping machine. The horse-drawn device was widely used and was soon followed by a host of mechanical harvesters.

McCORMICK

JAMES B. EADS

(American, 1820-1887)
Eads made many contributions to bridge engineering, but perhaps the most important was the development of pneumatic caissons. These were submersible chambers filled with compressed air which enabled workmen to sink the foundations of a bridge below the river bottom to supporting bedrock.

FREDERICK SIEMENS

(German, 1826-1904)
Siemens and his brothers developed the regenerative furnace still widely used today in refining steel by the economical open-hearth process. The furnace uses hot waste gases to preheat incoming fuel and air, thus conserving heat and melting impurities so that they rise and can be separated from the steel.

OTTO

NIKOLAUS A. OTTO

(German, 1832-1891)
In 1876 Otto built the first entirely successful internal-combustion gas engine and thereby made possible the development of the automobile. The machines gained immediate popularity, and Otto opened a factory which turned out 50,000 engines within 17 years.

WILLIAM LE BARON JENNEY

(American, 1832-1907)
An architect as well as engineer, Jenney developed the steel and iron frames that made skyscrapers a reality. Previously, the height of a building was limited because its weight had to be supported by heavy masonry walls. But Jenney's frames, prototypes of those used in modern skyscrapers, were light yet strong enough to support buildings of great height.

JENNEY

ERNEST SOLVAY

(Belgian, 1838-1922)
A pioneer chemical engineer, Solvay devised a new way to produce soda ash (sodium carbonate) from brine, limestone and ammonia. Still in use today, the Solvay process is extremely economical because most of the materials it employs are recovered for reuse.

THOMAS A. EDISON

(American, 1847-1931)
Best known for inventing the incandescent light bulb, Edison was also one of the first to apply the techniques of systems engineering. His career marks the transition between trial-and-error engineering and present-day scientific team efforts.

EDISON

FREDERICK W. TAYLOR

(American, 1856-1915)
Taylor is the man who introduced efficiency, or "scien-

194

tific management" methods, to industry. While working in a Philadelphia steel plant, he performed the first time-and-motion studies of factory workers, improved steel-making techniques, developed new tools, and suggested the incentive pay system.

FRANK SPRAGUE

SPRAGUE

(American, 1857-1934)
Sprague probably contributed more to the growth of electric rapid transit systems than any other man. He developed electric trolley cars and built the first successful trolley line in 1888. Sprague worked out the system of motors that permits either unified control of an entire train from the lead car or independent operation of individual cars. He was also instrumental in developing the electric elevator.

LEO H. BAEKELAND

BAEKELAND

(Belgian-American, 1863-1944)
In 1907 Baekeland initiated the modern age of plastics when he heated phenol and formaldehyde under pressure to produce Bakelite, the first truly synthetic plastic. The material has proved so versatile that it has been used for everything from lacquer to automobile parts.

HENRY FORD

FORD

(American, 1863-1947)
Ford put a whole nation on wheels by showing how to manufacture durable, practical and inexpensive automobiles. He developed simple designs that made repairs easy, sought materials that would stand up on rutted wagon trails, and pioneered assembly-line production of standardized units.

WRIGHT BROTHERS

(American, Wilbur 1867-1912; Orville 1871-1948)
The Wrights were among the first to use scientific experiments to solve an engineering problem. Before they flew the first powered airplane, they spent years working out laws of aerodynamics.

MARCONI

GUGLIELMO MARCONI

(Italian, 1874-1937)
In 1901 Marconi astounded the world by sending the first transatlantic wireless message. Applying the theory of radio waves which had been established a few years earlier, he developed the apparatus to make wireless telegraphy practical. He spent the rest of his life promoting and improving radio telegraphy.

CHARLES F. KETTERING

(American, 1876-1958)
Kettering was among the outstanding figures in the development of the automobile. Perhaps his most important invention was the self-starter, which ended the reliance on muscles to start a heavy engine and thus opened driving to women.

VLADIMIR ZWORYKIN

ZWORYKIN

(Russian-American, 1889-   )
Zworykin is largely responsible for making television a practical reality. Among his many contributions was the iconoscope, an electronic scanner similar to those now used in television cameras.

EDWIN H. ARMSTRONG

(American, 1890-1954)
Armstrong made many contributions to radio engineering, the most important of which was the invention of FM radio. He also worked out the superheterodyne circuit, the basic circuit used in AM radios today.

DONALD W. DOUGLAS SR.

DOUGLAS

(American, 1892-   )
In 1935 Douglas and a small group of engineers designed and built the DC-3, the first airplane to earn a profit flying passengers. Setting new standards of safety and dependability, it made commercial air travel practical.

PHILO T. FARNSWORTH

FARNSWORTH

(American 1906-   )
When he was 15 years old, Farnsworth invented a revolutionary electronic scanning device for TV cameras.

FURTHER READING

General

Love, Albert, and James Saxon Childers, eds., *Listen to Leaders in Engineering*. McKay, 1965.

*MacKendrick, Paul, *The Mute Stones Speak*. St. Martin's Press, 1960.

*Whinnery, John R., *The World of Engineering*. McGraw-Hill, 1965.

History of Engineering

Agricola, Georgius (Hoover, Herbert, and Lou H., translators), *De re metallica*. Dover, 1950.

†Burstall, Aubrey F., *A History of Mechanical Engineering*. The M.I.T. Press, 1965.

Dibner, Bern, *Moving the Obelisks*. Burndy Library, 1950.

*Kirby, Richard, and others, *Engineering in History*. McGraw-Hill, 1956.

Payne, Robert, *The Canal Builders*. Macmillan, 1959.

Singer, Charles, and others, eds., *A History of Technology*. Oxford University Press, Vol. I 1954, Vol. II 1957, Vol. III 1957.

†Straub, Hans, *A History of Civil Engineering*. The M.I.T. Press, 1964.

Fields of Engineering

Chapanis, Alphonse, *Man-Machine Engineering*. Wadsworth, 1965.

Lewis, Robert S., and George B.

Clark, *Elements of Mining* (3rd edition). John Wiley & Sons, 1964.

Nader, Ralph, *Unsafe at Any Speed*. Grossman, 1965.

Steinman, David B., and Sarah Ruth Watson, *Bridges and Their Builders*. Dover, 1957.

Talese, Gay, *The Bridge*. Harper & Row, 1964.

Engineering Achievements

*Bingham, Hiram, *Lost City of the Incas*. Duell, Sloan & Pearce, 1948.

Davis, Edward W., *Pioneering with Taconite*. Minnesota Historical Society, 1964.

†Dibner, Bern, *The Atlantic Cable*. Blaisdell Publishing Co., 1964.

†Josephson, Matthew, *Edison*. McGraw-Hill, 1963.

Future of Engineering

Deane, Philip, *Constantinos Doxiadis, Master Builder for Free Men*. Oceana, 1965.

Doxiadis, Constantinos A., *Architecture in Transition*. Oxford University Press, 1963.

Stenuit, Robert, *The Deepest Days*. Coward-McCann, 1966.

*Also available in paperback edition.

†Only available in paperback edition.

ACKNOWLEDGMENTS

The editors of this book are indebted to the following: Tetsuzo Akutsu and Paul Freed, Maimonides Hosp., Brooklyn; William Allen and Charles A. Fankhauser, American Cyanamid Co., Bound Brook, N.J.; the following persons from Edison National Historic Site, W. Orange, N.J.: Harold S. Anderson, Curator, Norman R. Speiden, Supervisory Museum Curator, Melvin J. Weig, Supt.; the following persons from M.I.T.: Raymond F. Baddour, Samuel W. Bodman III, Robert Byers, Charles Stark Draper, Harold E. Edgerton, Peter Elias, Anthony P. French, Peter Griffith, Robert J. Hansen, Harold S. Mickley, Charles L. Miller, Henry M. Paynter, Ascher H. Shapiro, Barry Unger, Bruce D. Wedlock, Francis Wylie; R. R. Beebe, Eugene Phfleider and Frank Wright, Minnesota School of Mines, U. of Minnesota, Minn.; S. C. Bottfeld, General Electric Co., Schenectady, N.Y.; Jack Burby; Burndy Library, Norwalk, Conn.; the following persons from the Henry Ford Museum, Dearborn, Mich.: Frank Caddy, Dir. of Administration, Frank Davis, Curator of Communications Arts, James E. Jones, Mgr. of Press Relations, Charles Natzel, Donald A. Shelley, Exec. Dir., and John Still, Asst. Dir. of Collections; Alphonse Chapanis, Dept. of Psychology, The Johns Hopkins University, Balt.; Edmond E. Chapus, Pres., NEYRPIC, N.Y.C.; the following persons from Ford Motor Co., Dearborn, Mich.: Gordon Cook, Exec. Dir., Clifford E. Cox, Michael E. R. Davis, Hayes Holmes, Robert Kraehe, Roy C. Lunn, Joseph A. Madden, John Mayberry, Herbert L. Misch, Vice Pres., J. L. Sloan; Jacques-Yves Cousteau, Oceanographic Museum, Monaco; C. W. Cribbs, Brunswick Corp., Muskegan, Mich.; Richard L. Deininger and John Kessler, Bell Telephone Laboratories, Murray Hill, N.J.; T. G. Delaney, IBM, N.Y.C.; Angelos C. Demetriou, Vice Pres., Doxiadis Assoc. Inc., Wash., D.C.; Constantinos A. Doxiadis, Pres., and A. N. Tombazis, Asst. to the Pres., Doxiadis Assoc. Inc., Athens; Henry Dreyfuss, Industrial Designers, N.Y.C.; Jack Dunlap Jr. and Lee Valarie, Dunlap & Assoc., Darien, Conn.; Louis Evans, RCA, N.Y.C.;

the following persons from Grumman Aircraft Engineering Corp., Long Island, N.Y.: Saul Ferdman, Steven Kerekes and associates, Clifford Seitz; David Fischer, General Electric Co., Milwaukee; J. V. Foa, Rensselaer Polytechnic Inst., Troy, N.Y.; Ken Graham, William J. Donoghue Assoc., N.Y.C.; Nomer Gray, Ammann and Whitney, Consulting Engineers, N.Y.C.; Rex Gray and L. T. Isaacs, Douglas Aircraft Inc., Santa Monica, Calif.; John Gregory and William Robinson, Bell Telephone Laboratories, N.Y.C.; Bernard Kaplan, Bernard Kaplan Assoc. Inc., N.Y.C.; Frederick G. Kilgour, Associate Librarian, Yale U.; Jiro Kohara, Prof., Dept. of Architecture, Chiba U., Chiba, Japan; Melvin Kranzberg, Case Inst. of Technology, Cleveland; Ezra S. Krendel, Franklin Inst., Phila.; Kenneth R. Lightcap, Doremus & Co., N.Y.C.; A. H. Mayor, Curator of Prints, Oscar W. Muscarella and Andrew Oliver, Metropolitan Museum of Art, N.Y.C.; Minnesota Historical Society, St. Paul; Neil J. Mizen, Cornell Aeronautical Laboratories, Cornell U., Buffalo; Jesse Orlansky, Inst. for Defense Analysis, Wash., D.C.; Edward Peizer, Chief, Bio-Engineering Research, VA Center, N.Y.C.; Leo Plofker, James Ruderman, Consulting Engineers, N.Y.C.; Derek de Solla Price, Chairman, Dept. of History of Science and Medicine, Yale U.; Public Relations Depts. of American Telephone & Telegraph Co., Western Electric and Bell Telephone Laboratories; staff members of Western Electric plant, Allentown, Pa.; Frank Rowsome Jr.; Morton Schiff, Physics Dept., Yeshiva U., N.Y.C.; Edward Schmid and Donald Wright, Reserve Mining Co., Silver Bay, Minn.; Ann Shortess, Henry Dreyfuss, Industrial Designers, N.Y.C.; Madeline Edison Sloane, W. Orange, N.J.; Alvin C. Smith, Vice Pres., Birdair Structures Inc., Buffalo; Henry H. von Spreckelson, Bethlehem Steel Corp., Bethlehem, Pa.; Triborough Bridge and Tunnel Authority, N.Y.C.; John Truxal, Dean of Engineering, Polytechnic Inst., Brooklyn; Henry Vermillion, Atomic Energy Commission, Las Vegas; and Harold Work, National Academy of Sciences, Wash., D.C.

INDEX

Numerals in italics indicate a photograph or painting of the subject mentioned.

A

Accidents, automobile, annual deaths from, 26
Aerial photography, 146
Aerojet-General Corporation, 172
Aeronautical engineering, schooling, 91, *95*
Air, as source of raw materials, 130
Air brakes, railroad, 11-12, *13*
Air pollution, 174
Airplanes: beginnings of, 145, *147;* control-knob identification, 147, 154, *164-165;* design, structural vs. functional elements, 145, 146-147; fuel-gauge markings, 147; human-factors engineering, 147-148, 154, *164-165,* 168; instrument design and placement, *164-165;* steering apparatus, 148
Akers, William, *178-179*
Akutsu, Tetsuzo, 153
Albert, Prince Consort, 34
Aldrin, Edwin "Buzz," 78
Algae, as food source, 175
Aluminum, honeycomb, *23, 84*
Aluminum refining, 123
American Cyanamid Company, *97*
American Society of Heating Engineers, 94
Ammann, Othmar H., 15, 108, 117, 118, 120
Ammonia, sources of, 129, 130
Amphibious dredge, *12*
Anderson, Bronco Billy, 52
Andover, Me., radome at, *184-185*
Anglesey suspension bridge, 59
Anio Novus water system, *68-69*
Antennae, radar, BMEWS, 103-105, *map* 107, 184
Apollo, Program, 77-85; cost of, 78; outline of flight plan, 78, *80-81;* power supply, 174-175; rocket, 78, *79;* technical manpower for development of, 78; units (modules), 78, *79-81;* use of computers, 82-83. *See also* Lunar Module
Appian Way, *66-67*
Aqueducts: ancient Roman, 34, 57, *68-69;* Barton, 35; for canals, 34-35, *36;* Syrian, *63*
Arch, use in construction: pointed, 57, *72-73;* round, 57
Arkwright, Sir Richard, *193*
Armer, Paul, 177
Armstrong, Edwin H., *195*
Armstrong, Neil, 78, 85
Arsenic, sources of, 123
Artificial body organs, 150-153, 178
Artificial limbs, 161
Assembly-line production: beginnings of, 13; modern, *28-29*
Astronautical engineering, schooling, 91, *95. See also* Apollo, Project; Lunar Excursion Module
Atomic Energy Commission, 95
Atomic reactors, 126-127, 174; cooling system research, *94-95*
Automation, 107; oil refining, 107; telephone information service, 149-150. *See also* Computers
Automobile accidents, annual deaths from, 26
Automobile engineering, 16, *17-31;* body engineering, *18-19;* chassis testing, *22-23;* engine engineering, *20-21;* of future, *24-25;* safety engineering, *26-27;* steel inspection, *19*
Automobile-guidance systems, future, 24
Automobile manufacture, assembly-line production, *28-29*
Automobiles: and air pollution, 174; body design, *18-19;* carburetors, 21; computerized, 24; cooling systems, 21; early, *25,* 123; engines, *20-21,* 174-175; fuel-cell powered, 174-175; fuel-gauge markings, 147; of future, *24-25,* 174-175; human-factors engineering, 147, 148, *159,* 168-169; ignition-system circuits, present vs. future, 24, 25; lights, *24-25;* seat belts, *26-27;* seat design, *159;* steering apparatus, 25, 26, 148; visual perception tests, during driving, *168-169*
Aviation. *See* Airplanes; Flight
Ayres, Eugene, 107

B

Babel, Tower of, 65
Babylonia, 62, 65
Baekeland, Leo H., *195*
Ballistic Missile Early Warning System (BMEWS), 77, 101, 103-106, *map* 107; stations, 104
Banking service, computerization of, 176-177
Barton Aqueduct, 35
Baylor College of Medicine, Texas, 152
Beetle, eyes and vision of, 146
Bell Laboratories, 150, 156, *157*
Bell Telephone System, 149
Belluschi, Pietro, 103
Beneficiation of ores, 141, 142
Benson, A. F., *136*
Bessemer steel process, 37, 38
Beth Israel Hospital, Boston, 151
Bethlehem Iron Company, 37-38
Bioengineering, 145. *See also* Bionics engineering; Human-factors engineering; Medical engineering
Bionics engineering, 145-147
BMEWS. *See* Ballistic Missile Early Warning System
Body contour studies, in human-factors engineering, *148-149, 155, 158-159*
Bogie, unidentified object in sky, 105
Bosch, Karl, 130
Boston: Beth Israel Hospital, 151; Massachusetts General Hospital, *93*
Bourges, France, Cathedral of St. Etienne, *72-73*
Bowers, David, 152
Boyd, T. A., 123-126
Brakes, pneumatic, on railroads, 11-12, *13*
Bridges: ancient Roman, 57; suspension, 14, 15, 58-59, 108, *109-119;* Verrazano-Narrows, 15, 108, *109-119*
Bridgewater, Duke of, 34-35
Brindley, James, *32,* 34-37, *193;* Bridgewater canal of, 34-*36;* Grand Trunk Canal of, 36
Bromine: as gasoline additive, 125; source of, 125, 130, 175
Brooklyn, N.Y., Maimonides Hospital, 152, 153
Brown, Edmund G. (Pat), 172, *cartoon* 174
Brunel, Isambard K., *194*
Buchanan, James, 60
Buffalo, N.Y., Veterans Administration Hospital, 152
Buttress, flying, 57, *58, 72, 73*
By-products, use of wastes for, 123, 129, 130, 131

C

Cables, transatlantic, *map* 60, 61
Calcium carbonate, source of, *122*
California, experiments in systems analysis of urban problems, 172-173, *cartoon* 174
Camera, aerial, 146
Canals: aqueducts for, 34-35, *36;* Brindley's Bridgewater, 34-*36;* Brindley's Grand Trunk, 36; Grand Canal of Languedoc, 34; lining of, 35; tunnels for, 36
Car-guidance systems, future, 24
Carburetors, automobile, 21
Carnot, Nicolas Léonard Sadi, 9
Cars. *See* Automobiles
Carthaginians, 66
Castles, medieval, 57-58
Cathedrals, Gothic, 57, *58, 72-73*
C-Curity Placket Fastener, early zipper, *14*
Central Valley, Calif., pollution problems, 174
Chair design, *148, 158-159*
Character traits, engineers', 9-10, 15
Chardack, William M., 152
Chassis tests, automobile, *22-23*
Chemical engineering, 21, 91, 96, 98, *122,* 123-126, 130-131
Cheops Pyramid. *See* Great Pyramid of Gizeh
Ch'in Shih Hwang Ti, Chinese Emperor, 56
China, Great Wall, 56-57

Chlorella pyrenoidosa, algae, 175
Cities. *See* Urban belts; Urban planning; Urbanization
Civil engineering, schooling, 91, *95,* 98. *See also* Bridges; Canals; Skyscrapers; Structural engineering; Urban planning
Civilizations, ancient, 33, 55-57, 62, *63-71,* 74
Clay, puddled, as canal lining, 35
Clear, Alaska, BMEWS station at, 104
Cleveland Clinic, Cleveland, Ohio, 152
Climate control, by domes, 105, 178, *184-185*
Cobalt, ocean-bottom deposits of, 175
Cohen, Rose, 145, 150, 151, 152, 153
Colleges, engineering, 86; computer availability, 93; recruitment of graduates from, 98. *See also* Education of engineers; Massachusetts Institute of Technology
Command Module, Apollo Program, 78, *79-81,* 83, 174-175
Communications by laser beam, *180-181;* by satellites, 184
Computers: in cars of future, *24;* potential dangers to society, 177; and revolution in engineering, 101; role in BMEWS, 104, 105, 106; at schools of engineering, *92-93;* significance of transistors in, 106; systems analysis of urban problems by, 172-174; time-sharing of, 93, 171, *173,* 176; use of, in assembly-line production, 29; use of, in space flight, 82-83; use of, in telephone information service, 149-150; various future uses of, *170,* 171, *173,* 176-177, 181
Connecticut Light and Power Company, 128
Conservation of natural resources, 123, 126, 128, 130-131
Consolidated Edison, nuclear reactor at Indian Point, N.Y., 127
Cooke, William, 59
Cooling systems, atomic reactors, 94; automobile, 21
Coordinatograph, *18,* 19
Copper mining, 123, 134; ocean bottom, 175
Corliss, Henry, 34
Corliss engine, 34
Cotton gin, 13
Coucy, castle of, 57-58
Coutinho, John, 81, 82
Crawshaw, Charles, and family, 171, 173
Crime prevention, systems analysis of, 172
Cryogenerator, 189
Cumae, ancient Greek tunnel at, 54

D

Dam building, 14
Darby, Abraham, 58
Data processing. *See* Computer; Information processing
Davis, Edward W., *136-137,* 138, *142*
DC-8 jet transport plane, instruments and controls, *164-165*
Dearborn, Mich., *30-31,* Museum, 44-47
De Bakey, Michael, 152-153
Defense system, radar, *map* 107. *See also* Ballistic Missile Early Warning System
De Forest, Lee, 10
Deininger, Richard L., 149-150
DEW. *See* Distant Early Warning
Dickson, Andrew, 94
Distant Early Warning (DEW) Line, *map* 107
Dopant, transistors, 107
Douglas, Donald W. Sr., *195*
Dow Chemical Company, 125
Doxiadis, Constantinos A., *186, 187*
Dredging scow, *12*
Dreyfuss, Henry, *156*
Driving perception tests, *168-169*
Dvorak, August, 148
Dynamometer, *20-21*

E

Eads, James B., *194*
Eastman, George, 52
Echolocating systems: in porpoise, 145-146; sonar, 146
Ecole Polytechnique, Paris, 86
Edgerton, Harold, 88
Edison, Thomas Alva, 39, 40, *41, 42,* 126, *194;* education of, 40; *41;* library of, *41;* Menlo Park laboratory of, *44-45,* 47; inventions of, *38-39,* 40, *42-43, 44, 46-53*
Education and the computer, 171, 177
Education of engineers: early 20th Century, *11;* federal grants and aid, 92, 94, 95; field work, 96, *97;* graduate study, *94-95, 97,* 98; grants by private industry, 94; high school, 88; history of, 86; M.I.T., 86, *87-99;* 19th Century, 38; refresher courses, *96;* specialization, 91, *94-95,* 98
Edwards, M. Lowell, 151
Efficiency, quest for, 123-131: in power production, 124-130; use of wastes for by-products, 123, 129, 130, 131
Egypt, ancient: prestige of engineers of, 33; pyramid-building, 33-34, 55-56
Einstein, Albert, 88
Electric light, invention of, 40, 44, *46-47. See also* Lighting systems
Electric pen, Edison's, *43*
Electric typewriter, 148
Electrical distribution systems, circuitry, *38-39*
Electrical engineering, 98; rise of, 33, 39, 40, *42, 46-49,* 55, 59-61; schooling, 91, *96,* 98
Electricity, production of: fuel economy in, 126-128; power sources, 126, *127,* 128, 174-175. *See also* Atomic reactors; Geothermal power; Hydroelectric power; Tidal power
Electrodyne Company, 151
Electronics, 98, 104, 151-152. *See also* Computers; Radar; Transistors
Ellet, Charles, 14
Emery Roth and Sons, 102
Empirical engineering, 33, 37-39
Engineer(s): compared to scientist, 9; general characteristics of, 9-10, 15; origin of term, 55
Engineering, goals of, compared with goals of science, 9
Engineering as a Career, 1916 manual, *11*
Engineering schools. *See* Colleges, engineering; Education of engineers
Engines: automobile, *20-21,* 174-175; fuel-cell, 174-175; jet, *183;* lunar module, 78, 81, 82, 84, 85; nuclear, 127, 174; railroad of future, 178, *183. See also* Steam engine; Steam turbine
England: canal system, 35-36; Industrial Revolution in, 33
Ethyl, gasoline additive, 125
Etruscans, 57, 66
Evans, Oliver, 12, 37
Explosives production, 130

F

Farnsworth, Philo Taylor, 10-11, *195*
Federal grants and aid, to engineering schools, 92, 94, 95
Ferdman, Saul, *79*
Fertilizer production, 130
Field, Cyrus W., 60, *61*
Fischer, David, 152
Fish: herding and raising of, 175; sensitivity to electrical changes, 145
Flight, early attempts, 145, *146-147*
Flying buttress, 57, *58, 72, 73*
Flying train, *182-183*
Foa, Joseph V., *182,* 183
Fontana, Domenico, 57
Food supply of future, 171, 175-176, 178
Ford, Henry, 123, 193, *195*
Ford Model T, 123
Ford Motor Company, *17-31;* annual production figure, 29; Mustang, 16, 17, *28-31;* number of workers, 29
Ford V-8 engine, *20-21*
Forman, Hugh, 152
Fortresses: Inca, 62, *70-71;* medieval, 57-58
Franklin, George, 85
Franklin Institute, Philadelphia, 148

French, Anthony, *88-89*
Fritz, John, 37-38, 39
Fuel cell, 174-175
Fuel gauges, marking of, 147
Fuels, economic use of: in electric power production, 126-128; gasoline, 124-126; geothermal power plants, 128-130; testing *21;* uranium, 126-127
Fulton, Robert, 40
Furniture design, *148, 155, 158-159*
Fylingdales Moor, England, BMEWS station at, 104

G

Galvanometer, mirror, 60-61
Gas turbine engine, for trucks, 21
Gasoline: in fuel cells, 175; no-knock high-test, development of, 123-126
Gavin, Joseph G. Jr., 80, 81
General Electric Company, medical engineering, 152
General Motors Corporation, 9; gasoline research, 124-125
Generator, Edison's, *48*
George Washington Bridge, Hudson River, 108
Geothermal power plants, 128-130
Geysers, power plants at, 128-130
Glider, of Lilienthal, *147*
Gold mining, 134, 138
Goodyear, Charles, 10
Gordon, T. J., 175
Gothic cathedrals, 57, *58, 72-73*
Graduate engineers: annual number of, vs. demand, 86; recruitment, 98
Graduate study, *94-95, 97,* 98
Grand Central Office Building, New York City, 102, *103*
Grand Coulee Dam, 14, 174
Grand Trunk Canal, England, 36
Granite block, cutting, Incan method, *71*
Great Eastern, the, 61
Great Pyramid of Gizeh, 33-34, 55-56
Great Train Robbery, The, 52-53
Great Wall, China, 56-57
Greatbatch, Wilson, 152
Greece, ancient, 33, 57, 66; tunnel of Fifth Century B.C., *54*
Gropius, Walter, 103
Grumman Aerospace Corporation, work on LM, 78-85

H

Haber, Fritz, 130
Haber-Bosch method of nitrate production, 130
Hall, Charles Martin, 123
Hammurabi, King of Babylon, 62
Handbook engineering, 33, 38-39, 77
Hanging Gardens of Babylon, 65
Hasselstein, Bernhard, 146
Heart, artificial, 152-153, 178
Heart-lung machine, 150
Heart pacemaker, artificial, 145, 150, 151-152
Heart valve, artificial, 151, *152, 179*
Helicable, 152
Helicopter design, research, *95*
Heliport, Pan Am Building, New York City, 101, *103*
Helmer, Olaf, 175
Hematite ore, 132, *134-135,* 136, 141
Herrmann, Herb, *95*
Hertz, Heinrich, 9
High school, science education in, 88
High-test gasoline, development of, 123-126
Highway radio signals, 168
Highway signs, 154, *166-167*
Hoist, salt mine, *74-75*
Holmes, Dyer Brainerd, 104, 106
Home, use of computer in, 171, *173,* 176
Honeycomb aluminum, *23, 84*
Hoover, Herbert, 33
Hoover Dam, 14
Household robots, 176
Houston, Texas, NASA Manned Spacecraft Center at, 80, 82
Human-factors engineering, *144,* 145, 147-150, 154, *155-169;* airplanes, 147-148, 154, *164-165,* 168; artificial limbs, 161; automobiles, 147, 148, *159, 168-169;* body contour studies, *148-149, 155, 158-159;* chair design, *158-159;* driving perception tests, *168-169;* habit patterns and, 148-149; Lunar Module, 81, 84-85; man-imitating machines, *162-163;* mattress construction, *155;* road signs, 154, *166-167;* telephone design and service, 149-150, 154, *156-157;* typewriter keyboard design, 148; walking-motion study, *160-161*

Hydroelectric power, 126, *127,* 128; and pumped storage, 127-128
Hydrogen fuel cell, 175

I

IBM System /360, computer, 176
Icarus, 145
Iceland, utilization of geysers in, 128, 129
Ignition-system circuits, automobile, *24,* 25
Incas: hanging bridges of, 59; mountain fortresses of, 62, *70-71*
Indian Point, N.Y., nuclear reactor at, 127
Industrial Revolution, 33, 34, 37, 55, 58, 59, 74; second (automation), 107
Industry: campus recruitment of engineers by, 98; grants to engineering colleges, 94
Information processing: educational advantages, 177; and laser beam, *181;* potential dangers to society, 177; systems analysis of problems of, 172, *cartoon 174*
Instrumentation engineer, 19
Interchangeable parts, introduction of concept of, 13
Intercontinental missiles, attack detection, 104, 105, *map 107*
Iron ore mining, 58, 132, *133-143;* hematite, 132, *134-135,* 136, 141; taconite, 123, 132, *136-143*
Islamabad, Pakistan, city planning, *186-187*
"Ivory hunters," 98

J

Jenney, William Le Baron, *194*
Jet propulsion, for trains, 173, 178, *182-183*
Jones, Jack, 173
Jordan, Fred, *136*
Judson, Whitcomb, zipper of, *13-14*

K

Kantrowitz, Adrian, 152
Kelley, Thomas J., 80
Kelp, as food source, 175
Kelvin, Lord. *See* Thomson, Sir William
Kennedy, John F., 79
Kettering, Charles F., 124-126, 195
Khufu, Pharaoh, 55, 56
Khufu-onekh, 33, 55-56
Kidney, artificial, 150, 152
Killingworth Colliery, 37
Kinetophone, 52
Kinetoscope, 52
Kiss, The, early movie, *52-53*
Kohara, Jiro, *148, 158, 159*
Kolff, Willem, 152
Krendel, Ezra S., 148

L

Land use problems, systems analysis of, 173
Langley Field, Va., NASA research center at, 82
Languedoc, Grand Canal of, 34
Larderel, Francesco de, 129
Larderello, Italy, geothermal power plant, 128, 129; insignia, *129*
Laser beam, *180-181;* creation of, *180;* defined, 181; use in communications, *map 180*
LM. *See* Lunar Module
Leonardo da Vinci, 145, 147; sketch of wing by, *147*
Light bulb, incandescent, invention of, 40, 44, *46-47*
Lighting systems, early, 39, *48-49;* fuel consumption, 126; types of circuits, *38-39*
Lilienthal, Otto, with glider, *147*
Limbs, artificial, 161
Liverpool, England, Brindley's canal at, 35-36
Lockheed Missiles & Space Company, 172
Los Angeles, air pollution in, 174
Lunar Module (LM), Apollo Program, 78, *79-81,* 82-85; advance testing, 82-83; ascent engine, 78, 80, 81, 82; communications system, 81, 82-83; cost of, 80; descent engine, 80, 81, 82, 84, 85; human-factors system, 81, 84-85; landing-gear subsystem, 83-*84;* project management, 80; protection for landing gear, 84; reliability system, 81-82; simulated control panel, *76;* technical manpower for develop-

ment of, 80; various systems and subsystems, 81; visibility problem, 84-85; weight problems, 81, 84-85
Lunn, Roy, 17

M

MAC, Project, *92-93*
McCormick, Cyrus, *194*
Machu Picchu, Incan city, *70-71*
Mackie, Janet, *21*
Magnesium, sources of, *122,* 130-131, 175
Magnetic separation, in iron mining, 123, 136, *137-138, 141*
Magnetite, 138, 142; extraction from ore, *137-138,* 141; pellets, *142-143*
Maimonides Hospital, Brooklyn, N.Y., 152, 153
Man Amplifier project, 162, *163*
Manchester, England, Brindley's canal at, 34-36
Manganese, ocean-bottom deposits of, 175
Manhattan: early electric system in, 48; Pan Am Building, 101-*103;* skyscrapers, *100*
Manned Spacecraft Center, NASA, Houston, Texas, 80, 82
Manufacturing engineer, *28,* 29
Marconi, Guglielmo, 9, *195*
Marine engineering, 91
Mass production techniques: beginnings of, 13; modern, *28-29*
Massachusetts General Hospital, Boston, *93*
Massachusetts Institute of Technology, 86, *87-99;* breakdown of fields of engineering, 91; Center for Advanced Engineering Study, 96; computer training at, *92-93;* examinations, *98-99;* freshman year, *88-89,* 91; graduate study, *94-95, 97,* 98; number of students, 86; refresher courses, 96; sophomore year, 90, 91, 94
Mattress construction, study for, 155
Maudslay, Henry, 193
Mechanical engineering, schooling, 91, *94-95*
Medical engineering, 145, 150-153, *179*
Medical research, role of computer in, *93*
Menlo Park, N.J., Edison's laboratory at, 40, *44-45,* 47, 48
Mesabi Range iron mining: hematite, *134-135,* 136; taconite, *136-143*
Mesopotamia, 33, 64
Metallurgical engineering, 16, 91
Metals, ocean-bottom mining of, 175
Microwaves, in communication, 181
Middle Ages: cathedrals of, 57, *58, 72-73;* engineering, 55, 57-58, 72
Midgley, Thomas Jr., 123-124, 126
Midvale Steel Company, 38
Mineral deposits on ocean bottom, 175, 178
Mining: 15th Century hoist, *74-75;* low-grade ores, extraction techniques, 123, 136, *137-138, 141;* modern machinery, *137-143;* 19th Century, *133-135;* ocean bottom, 175, 178, 188; open-pit, 123, *134-135;* 16th to 18th Century innovations, 58, *59,* 74. *See also* Iron ore mining
Mirror galvanometer, 60-61
M.I.T. *See* Massachusetts Institute of Technology
Montlouis, France, solar furnace at, *190-191*
Moon landing, Apollo Program, *76,* 77-85; simulation, 82
Moonscape, at Houston, Texas, 82
Morrison, Philip, 88
Morse, Samuel F.B., 59
Motion pictures, invention of, 40, 52
Motion study, human body, *160-161*
Mullaney, Robert S., 80, 81
Multiple Access Computer (MAC), *92-93*
Mustang, car, *30-31;* development and manufacture of, 16, *17, 28-29*
Mylar, thermal protection on LM, 84

N

NASA, and Apollo Program, 79, 80, 82, 84, 85
Natural resources: conservation of, 123, 126, 128; in ocean, 130-131, 175-176, 178, 188; use of common (as air; seawater), 130-131
New York City: early electrical system in, 48, 126; metropolitan area highway and bridge system, *map* 111; Pan Am Building, 101-*103;* skyscrapers, *100;* Verrazano-Narrows Bridge, 15, 108, *109-119*
Newcomen, Thomas, 33
Niagara, the, 61

ment of, 80; various systems and subsystems, 81; visibility problem, 84-85; weight problems, 81, 84-85

Niagara Falls, suspension bridge at, 10; service bridge, 14
Nickel, ocean-bottom deposits of, 175
Nimes, France, aqueduct at, *69*
Nitrates, sources and production of, 130
No-knock gasoline, 123-126
NORAD. *See* North Atlantic Air Defense Command
Norias, waterwheels, *63*
North American Aviation, 172
North American Rockwell Corporation, Rocketdyne Division, Canoga Park, Calif., 80
North Atlantic Air Defense Command (NORAD), 104, *map 107*
Notre Dame, Paris, 101
Nuclear engineering, 91
Nuclear power, 174. *See also* Atomic reactors
Nuclear submarines, 127

O

Obelisk, moving of, 57
Ocean: as food source, 175-176; as future human habitat, 178, *188-189;* mining, 175, 178, 188; as source of raw materials, *122,* 125, 130-131, 175-176
Oil refining, 125; automation of, 107; by-products, 123, 130
Open-hearth steel process, 37
Orbiting Astronomical Observatory, Grumman, 80
Ore, beneficiation of, 141, 142. *See also* Iron ore; Mining
Organs, body, artificial, 150-153
Orukter Amphibolos, dredge, *12*
Oscilloscope, *90*
Otto, Nikolaus A., *194*
Oyster shells, as source of calcium carbonate, *122*

P

Pacemaker, heart, 145, 150, 151-152
Pan Am Building, New York City, 101-*103;* design, 102-103; foundation footings, 102, *103;* heliport, 101, *103;* statistics, 101
Panama Canal project, research, *95*
Parallel circuit, electrical distribution system, *38*
Parts interchangeability, introduction of concept of, 13
Pellets, iron, *138,* 141, *142-143*
Perception tests, during driving, *168-169*
Personality traits, engineers', 9-10, 15
Petroleum refining. *See* Oil refining
Philadelphia Centennial Exhibition, 34
Phonograph, invention of, 40, 44, *50-51*
Photography, aerial, 146
Pickford, Mary, 52
Pipeline transportation of future, 173
Pocket radio, transistors in, 106
Pollution problems, 174-175; systems analysis of, 172, *173-174*
Polymer chemistry, and artificial body organs, 153
Pont du Gard, Nimes, France, *69*
Pope, Franklin, 194
Population: urban migration of, *chart* 175, *maps* 176; world, in 2000, 171
Porpoise, echolocating system of, 145-146
Power production: quest for efficiency, 124-130; sources of future, 174-175, 178, *190-191.* See also Atomic reactors; Fuels; Geothermal power; Hydroelectric power; Solar energy; Tidal power
Professional Amateur, Boyd, 124
Professionalism in engineering, rise of, 33, 86
Project MAC, *92-93*
Puddling, clay, 35
Pumped storage, in electric power systems, 127-128
Pumps, in mining: reversible waterwheel, *59;* steam pump, 58, 74
Pyle, Wendell, 152
Pyramids, 33-34, 55-56

R

Rabinow, Jacob, 10
Racing-car engine, *20-21*
Radar, in North American defense system, 104-106, *map 107*
Radio: laser beam transmission, 181; transistorized, 106
Radio Corporation of America: and development of television, 11; work on BMEWS, 104-106
Radio signals, highway, 168
Radome, 105, *184-185*
Railroads: air brakes, 11-12, *13;*

beginnings of, 33, 37, 58; of future, 173, 178, *182-183*
Rance River, France, tidal power plant at, *127*, 128
Rand Corporation, 175, 177
Rathke, William, 80, 83
Records centralization: educational advantages, 177; potential dangers to society, 177; systems analysis of problems of, 172, *cartoon* 174
Recruitment, campus, 98
Refresher courses for engineers, *96*
Reichardt, Werner, 146
Relativity, theory of. 88
Rensselaer Polytechnic Institute, 86
Reserve Mining Company, taconite mining, *139-143*
Rice University, Texas, 178
Richmond, Va., early electric trolley system in, 13
Rickover, Hyman G., 127
Road radio signals, 168
Road signs, 154, *166-167*
Roads, ancient Roman, *66-67*
Robots, household, 176
Roebling, John, 10, *194*
Rome, ancient, 33, 57; aqueducts, 34, 57, *68-69;* engineers' tools, *8;* roads, *66-67;* water systems, *68-69*
Rosen, Mark, *96*
Rosen, Paul, *96*
Rosing, Boris, 11
Roth, Richard, 102-103
Ruderman, James, 102, 103
Russell, William Howard, 61

S

Safety engineering, automobile, *26-27*
St. Etienne, Cathedral of, Bourges, *72-73*
St. Lawrence hydroelectric power development, 77
Salt mine, hoist, *74-75*
San Francisco, pollution problems, 174
Satellites, communication, 184
Saturn V, rocket, 78, *79*
Savage, John Lucian, 14
Science, goals of, 9
Scientific engineering, 39, 86, 88
Scientist, compared to engineer, 9
Scully, Michael, *95*
Seat belts, *26-27*
Seawater, as source of raw materials, *122*, 125, 130-131, 175
Seaweed, as food source, 175
Series circuit, electrical distribution system, 38
Service Module, Apollo Program, 78, *79-81*, 174-175
Sherman, Howard, 84
Sholes, Christopher Latham, 148
Siemens, Frederick, 38, 194
Siemens-Martin open-hearth steel process, 38
Silicon transistors, 106-107
Silicone rubber, artificial heart valve

of, 151; as material for artificial heart, 153
Skyscrapers, *100*, 101-*103*
Sloan, Alfred P. Jr., 9
Smeaton, John, *193*
Smith, Arthur C., *96*
Soda ash, production of, *130*, 131
Solar energy, use of, 128, 190
Solar furnace, *190-191*
Solvay, Ernest, 130, 131, 194
Solvay process, *130*, 131
Sonar, 146
Space docking, 78, *81*, 83; test, *76*
Space-General Corporation, 172
Spacecraft systems, 77. *See also* Lunar Module
Sparkplug insulator, test of, *20*
Specialization, 9, 16, 91, *94-95*, 98
Sprague, Frank, 13, 39, *195*
Stanley, William, 48
Stapler, surgical, 15
Starr, Albert, 151
Steam engine, 33, 37, 58, 74; in amphibious dredge, *12;* Corliss, 34; of Watt, 33, 123
Steam pumps, mining, 58, 74
Steam turbine, 126-127
Steel, microscopic inspection of, *19*
Steel production, 58; Bessemer process, 37, 38; open-hearth process, 38
Steering apparatus, and human-factors engineering, 148
Stephenson, George, 37, *193*
Stevens Institute of Technology, 38
Stock ticker, Edison's, 42, *43*
Stokes-Adams disease, 151
Streetcars, invention of pole, 13
Strip-mining, 123, *134-135*
Structural engineering: Pan Am Building, 102-103; use of arch, 57, *72-73;* Verrazano-Narrows Bridge, 108, *109, 112-117*
Sugarcane fiber, by-products from, 123
Sumerian ziggurat, *64-65,* 101
Sunbury, Pa., early electrical distribution system, 39
Sundback, Gideon, zipper of, 14, *15*
Surgical stapler, 15
Suspension bridges, 10, 15, 58-59, 108, *109-119. See also* Verrazano-Narrows Bridge
Syracuse, N.Y., soda-ash production at, 131
Syrian waterwheel, ancient, 62, *63*
Systems analysis: of political and economic problems, 176; of urban problems, 172-174, *chart* 175
Systems engineering, 77-85, 93, 101, 172; basic rule of, 173-174; defined, 77; Lunar Module, 79, 81-85; Pan Am Building, 101-102

T

Taconite, 123, 132, *135*, 138-142; beneficiation of, 141, 142; iron content, 138; mining

techniques, 138-139
Taylor, Frederick W., 38, 194-195
Teamwork in engineering, rise of, 16, 61
Tektite Project, *188-189*
Telegraph: automatic. 42: Edison's inventions, *42-43;* invention by Morse, 59-60; multiplex, *42-43;* quadruplex, 42; transatlantic cables, *map* 60, 61; wireless, 9
Telephone: design, 149, *150*, 154, *156-157;* information service, computerization of, 149-150; laser beam transmission, 181
Television: beginnings of, 11; laser beam transmission, 181
Telford, Thomas, 33, 59, *193*
Tennessee Valley hydroelectric power development, 77
Tetraethyl lead, gasoline additive, 125
Textbook engineering, 33
The Geysers, Calif., geothermal power plant at, 128, 129-130
Theory of relativity, 88
Thermodynamics, 9
Thermonuclear power, 174
Thompson, John, *95*
Thomson, Sir William (Lord Kelvin), 60
Three-wire circuit, electrical distribution system, *39*
Thule, Greenland, BMEWS station at, 104-106
Ticker, stock, Edison's, 42, *43*
Tidal power plant, Rance River, France, *127*, 128
Toynbee, Arnold, 177
Transatlantic cables, *map* 60, 61
Transistors, 101, 106-107
Transportation: early feats of, with rudimentary tools, 55-56, 57, *74-75;* of future, 173, 178, *182-183;* problems of, in urban society, 171, 172, 173. *See also* Automobiles; Canals; Railroads
Trevithick, Richard, 33, 37
Trial-and-error engineering, 37-39, 57, 77, 82
Trolley pole, invention of, 13
Trucks, gas turbine engine for, 21
TRW Inc., Redondo Beach, Calif., 80
Tunnels: for 18th Century canal, 36; Greek, Fifth Century B.C., *54;* for transportation of future, 173, *182-183*
Typewriter keyboard, design of, 148

U

Underwater exploration, *188*
Underwater housing, 178, *188-189*
Unger, Barry, *91*
United Nations, international road signs of, 165
University of Illinois, 15
University of Minnesota, School of Mines, 136, *137*

University of Oregon, 151
Ur, Sumerian ziggurat at, *64-65,* 101
Urban belts, in U.S., *maps* 176; future transportation, *182-183*
Urban planning, *186-187*
Urbanization: problems of, 171, 172; statistics, *chart* 175; systems analysis, 172-174
U.S. Air Force: "Beetle," *162;* and BMEWS, 104
U.S. Atomic Energy Commission, 95
U.S. Navy, 95
Utility engineering, 126-130

V

Van Depoele, Charles, 13
Vanderbilt, Cornelius, 11-12
Vaults, Gothic cathedrals, 57, *72-73*
Verrazano-Narrows Bridge, New York Harbor, 15, 108, *109-119;* Brooklyn approaches, *110-111;* cables and cable anchorages, *114-117;* construction of, *109, 112-119;* as link in metropolitan highway system, *map* 111; roadway decks, *118-119;* towers and foundations, *109, 112-113;* traffic load, 111
Veterans Administration Hospital, Buffalo, N.Y., 152
Victoria, Queen, 60
Visual perception tests during driving, *168-169*
Volcanic power plants, 128-130

W

Waikato River, New Zealand, 129
Wairakei Valley, New Zealand, geothermal power plant at, 128, 129
Walking-motion study, *160-161*
Walsh, Homan, 14
Waste management, 174-175; systems analysis of problems of, 172, 173-174
Water systems, ancient Roman, *68-69*
Waterwheel, 74; ancient Syrian, 62, *63;* reversible, 16th Century, 59
Watt, James, 12, 33, 37, 40, 123, 126, *193*
West Orange, N.J., Edison's laboratory at, 40, *41, 50-51*
Westinghouse, George, 11, 48; air brakes of, 11-12, *13*
Wheatstone, Charles, 59
White Sands, N.M., testing of LM, 82
Whitney, Eli, 12-13, 40, *193*
Wieliczka, Poland, salt-mine hoist, *74-75*
Wolfson, Erwin S., 102-103
Wright, Orville and Wilbur, 145, *193,* 195

Z

Ziggurat, at Ur, *64-65,* 101
Zipper, development of, 13, *14-15*
Zoll, Paul, 151
Zworykin, Vladimir, 11, *195*

PICTURE CREDITS

The sources for the illustrations that appear in this book are shown below. Credits for the pictures from left to right are separated by commas, from top to bottom by dashes.

Cover—Ken Kay from D.P.I.

CHAPTER 1: 8—David Lees courtesy the Capitoline Museum, Rome. 11—The New York Public Library. 12—The Engineering-Transportation Library, University of Michigan. 13—Courtesy The Westinghouse Automatic Brake Company. 14—Courtesy Talon Inc. 15—Drawings by Otto van Eersel. 17 through 31—John Zimmerman.

CHAPTER 2: 32—Alan Clifton courtesy Salford Museum and Art Gallery, Lancashire, England. 36—Courtesy Radio Times Hulton Picture Library. 38, 39—Diagrams by Otto van Eersel. 41—Arnold Newman courtesy Edison National Historic Site, West Orange, New Jersey. 42, 43—Arnold Newman courtesy Henry Ford's Greenfield Village, Dearborn, Michigan, except left Arnold Newman courtesy Edison National Historic Site, West Orange, New Jersey. 44, 45, 46—Arnold Newman courtesy Henry Ford's Greenfield Village, Dearborn, Michigan. 47—Arnold Newman courtesy Edison National Historic Site, West Orange, New Jersey—Arnold Newman courtesy Henry Ford's Greenfield Village, Dearborn, Michigan. 48, 49—Arnold Newman courtesy Henry Ford's Greenfield Village, Dearborn, Michigan. 50 through 53—Arnold Newman courtesy Edison National Historic Site, West Orange, New Jersey.

CHAPTER 3: 54—Raymond V. Schoder, S.J. 57—The New York Public Library. 58—Drawing by Otto van Eersel. 59—From *De re metallica* by Georgius Agricola. 60, 61—The Burndy Library. 63—Harry Koundakjian. 64, 65—Hirmer Fotoarchiv, Munich. 66, 67—Map by Leslie Martin, James Burke—Dave Richards courtesy Yale University Audio Visual Center. 68, 69—Emmett Bright, Fritz Henle from Photo Researchers Inc. 70, 71—Douglas Faulkner, Kay Lawson from Rapho Guillumette—Marc and Evelyne Bernheim from Rapho Guillumette. 72, 73—Bibliothèque Nationale, Dmitri Kessel (2). 74, 75—Erich Lessing from Magnum.

CHAPTER 4: 76—Courtesy Grumman Aircraft Engineering Corporation, Bethpage, New York. 79 through 84—Drawings by Leslie Martin except pages 80, 81, drawings by Leslie Martin and Raymond Ripper. 87—Leonard McCombe. 88—James MaHood. 89—Leonard McCombe—James MaHood. 90 through 99—Leonard McCombe.

CHAPTER 5: 100—Lee Lockwood from Black Star. 103—Emory Roth and Sons and Leo Plofker of James Ruderman. 107—Map by Otto van Eersel. 109, 110—Barrett Gallagher. 111—Barrett Gallagher, map by Nicholas Fasciano. 112—Map by Nicholas Fasciano, Bethlehem Steel Corporation. 113—Bethlehem Steel Corporation, Barrett Gallagher. 114 through 121—Barrett Gallagher.

CHAPTER 6: 122—J. R. Eyerman courtesy Dow Chemical Company. 127—Drawing by Otto van Eersel. 129—from *Engineers Dream* by Willy Ley, Viking Press, New York. 130—Drawing by George V. Kelvin. 133 through 137—Courtesy The Minnesota Historical Society. 138, 139—Francis Miller except extreme right Jean Basgen. 140, 141—Jean Basgen. 142, 143—Francis Miller.

CHAPTER 7: 144—Charts from *The Measure of Man* © 1959 by Henry Dreyfuss, published by Whitney Publications, Inc. 146—Ambrosiana Library, Milan. 147—Bettmann Archive. 148—Courtesy Dr. Jiro Kohara, Chiba University, Japan. 149—Courtesy The Wright Air Development Center. 150—Drawings by Donald and Ann Crewes. 152—Drawings by Leslie Martin. 155—Drawing by Morris Kantor courtesy Dr. Jiro Kohara, Chiba University, Japan. 156—Courtesy Henry Dreyfuss, Anthony Wolff. 157—Courtesy The Bell Telephone Company. 158—Courtesy Dr. Jiro Kohara, Chiba University, Japan. 159—Courtesy Dr. Jiro Kohara, Chiba University, Japan, except top left Leon R. Lewandowski courtesy Institute of Design I.I.T. 160, 161—Courtesy Veterans Administration Regional Office, Prosthetics Center, New York. 162—Robert W. Kelley. 163—Ted Russell. 164, 165—Gordon Tenney. 166—Robert W. Kelley. 167—UNATIONS—Swiss National Tourist Office, Foto Giegel ONST. 168—Ted Russell courtesy Dunlap and Associates, Darien, Conn.—Anthony Wolff. 169—Ted Russell courtesy Dunlap and Associates, Darien, Conn.

CHAPTER 8: 170—Gordon Tenney. 173—Courtesy General Electric, Phoenix, Arizona. 174—Newton Pratt, Sacramento *Bee*. 175—Graph by Mana Maeda. 176—Maps by James Alexander. 179—Ralph Morse. 180, 181—Map by Nicholas Fasciano—drawing by Otto van Eersel—drawing by Nicholas Fasciano, Henry Groskinsky. 182—Ken Kay. 183—Drawings by Nicholas Fasciano (2)—Ken Kay. 184, 185—Drawing by Nicholas Fasciano, courtesy The American Telephone and Telegraph Co. 186, 187—Courtesy Doxiadis Associates, David Rubinger, drawings by Nicholas Fasciano. 188—Courtesy Les Requins Associés. 189—Courtesy Les Requins Associés—Philippe Cousteau © National Geographic Society—drawing by Nicholas Fasciano. 188, 189—Flip Schulke from Black Star. 190—Drawing by John Woods—Jean Marquis. 191—Jean Marquis. 193—Left drawing by Paul Calle—drawing by Paul Calle courtesy Culver Pictures Inc.—drawing by Paul Calle; right drawing by Paul Calle courtesy Bettmann Archive—drawing by Paul Calle. 194—Left drawing by Paul Calle courtesy The Institute of Civil Engineers—drawing by Paul Calle courtesy United Press International—drawing by Paul Calle courtesy Bettmann Archive; right drawing by Paul Calle courtesy Culver Pictures Inc.—drawing by Paul Calle courtesy Wide World Photos. 195—Left drawing by Paul Calle courtesy *The New York Times* Studio—drawing by Paul Calle courtesy Union Carbide—drawing by Paul Calle courtesy Greystone Studios Inc.; right drawings by Paul Calle except third from top drawing by Paul Calle courtesy United Press International. Back cover—Drawing by Mana Maeda.